# SP CE & EARTH
## SCIENCE
### STUDENT ACTIVITIES

For use with
**Third Edition**

**BJU PRESS**
Greenville, South Carolina

NOTE: The fact that materials produced by other publishers may be referred to in this volume does not constitute an endorsement of the content or theological position of materials produced by such publishers. Any references and ancillary materials are listed as an aid to the student or the teacher and in an attempt to maintain the accepted academic standards of the publishing industry.

**SPACE AND EARTH SCIENCE STUDENT ACTIVITIES**
**For use with Third Edition**

**R. Terrance Egolf, CDR, USN (retired)**
**Franklin S. Hall, MA**

**Contributing Writers**
Linda Shumate
Rachel Santopietro

**Consultant**
Eugene Chaffin, PhD

**Project Editor**
Michael Santopietro

**Compositors**
Peggy Hargis
Kelley Moore

**Cover Designers**
John Bjerk
Aaron Dickey

**Designers**
John Bjerk
Kristin Boyles
Aaron Dickey
David Siglin

**Photo Acquisition**
Brenda Hansen
Joyce Landis
Susan Perry
Visuals Unlimited

**Illustrators**
Peter Crane
Aaron Dickey
Terrance Egolf
Preston Gravely
James Hargis
Brian D. Johnson
Jonathan Johnson
Nathan Kirsop
Sarah Lyons
David Schuppert

**Project Manager**
Victor Ludlum

Photograph Credits appear on page SA295.

Originally published as *Student Activities in EARTH SCIENCE*
Revised by David Anderson, PhD, and Richard Seeley, MS.

Produced in cooperation with the Bob Jones University Division of Natural Science of the College of Arts and Science.

© 2005 BJU Press
Greenville, South Carolina 29614
First Edition © 1986 BJU Press
Second Edition © 1993, 1999 BJU Press

15  14  13  12  11  10  9  8  7  6  5  4  3  2

# CONGRATULATIONS!

Your search for the very best educational materials available has been completely successful! You have a textbook that is the culmination of decades of research, experience, prayer, and creative energy.

### The Facts
Nothing overlooked. Revised and updated. Facts are used as a springboard to stimulate thoughtful questions and guide students to broader applications.

### The Foundation
Nothing to conflict with Truth and everything to support it. Truth is the pathway as well as the destination.

### The Fun
Nothing boring about this textbook! Student (and teacher) might even forget it's a textbook! Brimming with interesting extras and sparkling with color!

# CONTENTS

SCIENCE

STUDENT ACTIVITIES

A

# 1 NATURAL SCIENCES AND THE CHRISTIAN

Applications

## 1A The First Law of Thermodynamics

One of the foundational laws of science is the first law of thermodynamics. This principle states that matter and energy can be neither created nor destroyed. According to another well-known principle of physics, matter and energy are just different forms of the same thing. Therefore, the first law means that no form of matter or energy is appearing or disappearing today anywhere in the universe. This is just another way of restating Genesis 2:1: "Thus the heavens and the earth were finished, and all the host of them."

Though energy cannot be created nor destroyed, it can change from one kind of energy to another. There are eight kinds of energy that you are probably familiar with. They are mechanical, electrical, magnetic, thermal (heat), sound, chemical, nuclear, and electromagnetic (light). Mechanical energy can be subdivided into the energy of moving things (kinetic energy) and the energy due to an object's physical position or condition (potential energy). When a process changes one form of energy into another, the new form of energy can be observed in some way, either by instruments or by our senses.

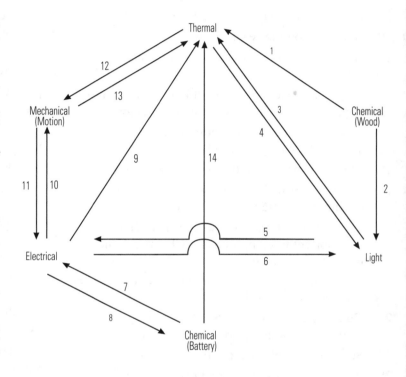

*Directions*: For each of the energy changes shown in the diagram, give an example of a process or a device that involves the energy change in the direction indicated by the arrow.

1. _____

2. _____

3. _____

4. _____

5. _____

6. _____

7. _____

8. _____

9. _____

10. _____

11. _____

12. _____

13. _____

14. _____

Applications

# 1B Philosophy of Science

*Directions*: Complete the crossword puzzle.

## Across

5. The ____ is scientifically accurate.

6. Genesis 8:22 indicates that there are some things that man will never be able to ____.

7. God created the heaven and the earth out of ____.

9. God ____ on the seventh day.

11. A measure of the disorderliness of a system is called ____.

12. ____ is a process by which things form (and then improve) by themselves without a Creator.

16. ____ is the belief that conditions today are the same as they always have been.

19. Christians believe in the Genesis account of ____.

20. The Bible provides the only proper ____ for conducting scientific investigations.

21. The interpretation of the word *was* in Genesis 1:2 is important to compromising Christians who believe the ____ theory.

22. ____ evolution is a compromise between the Bible and evolutionary science.

23. God breathed into man "the breath of ____; and man became a living soul" (Gen. 2:7).

24. Scientists are often at the frontier of human ____.

29. Anything that has mass and occupies space is called ____.

30. ____ cannot give us permanent, absolute truth as the Bible does.

## Down

1. Genesis 1:28 tells us to ____ the earth.

2. God created the earth for the ____ of mankind (Ps. 68:19).

3. According to Genesis 1:28, man is to have ____ over the living things.

4. Evolution is a ____, not an absolute truth.

8. The ____ drastically changed the world.

10. One term that describes the tendency in nature for systems to become less ordered or organized is ____.

13. ____ reasoning is also called "begging the question."

14. The law of ____ of mass and energy states that the total quantity of matter plus energy in the universe remains the same.

15. A Christian who holds to six 24-hour, end-to-end days of Creation has a ____ view of Scripture.

17. Matthew 19:4 clearly teaches that ____ and woman were divinely created as such from the very beginning.

18. A ____ is a mistake in reasoning.

25. The ability to do work is called ____.

26. Genesis 1:1 states, "In the beginning ____ created the heaven and the earth."

27. God created the entire universe in six ____.

28. Ultimately, the topic of origins must be accepted by ____.

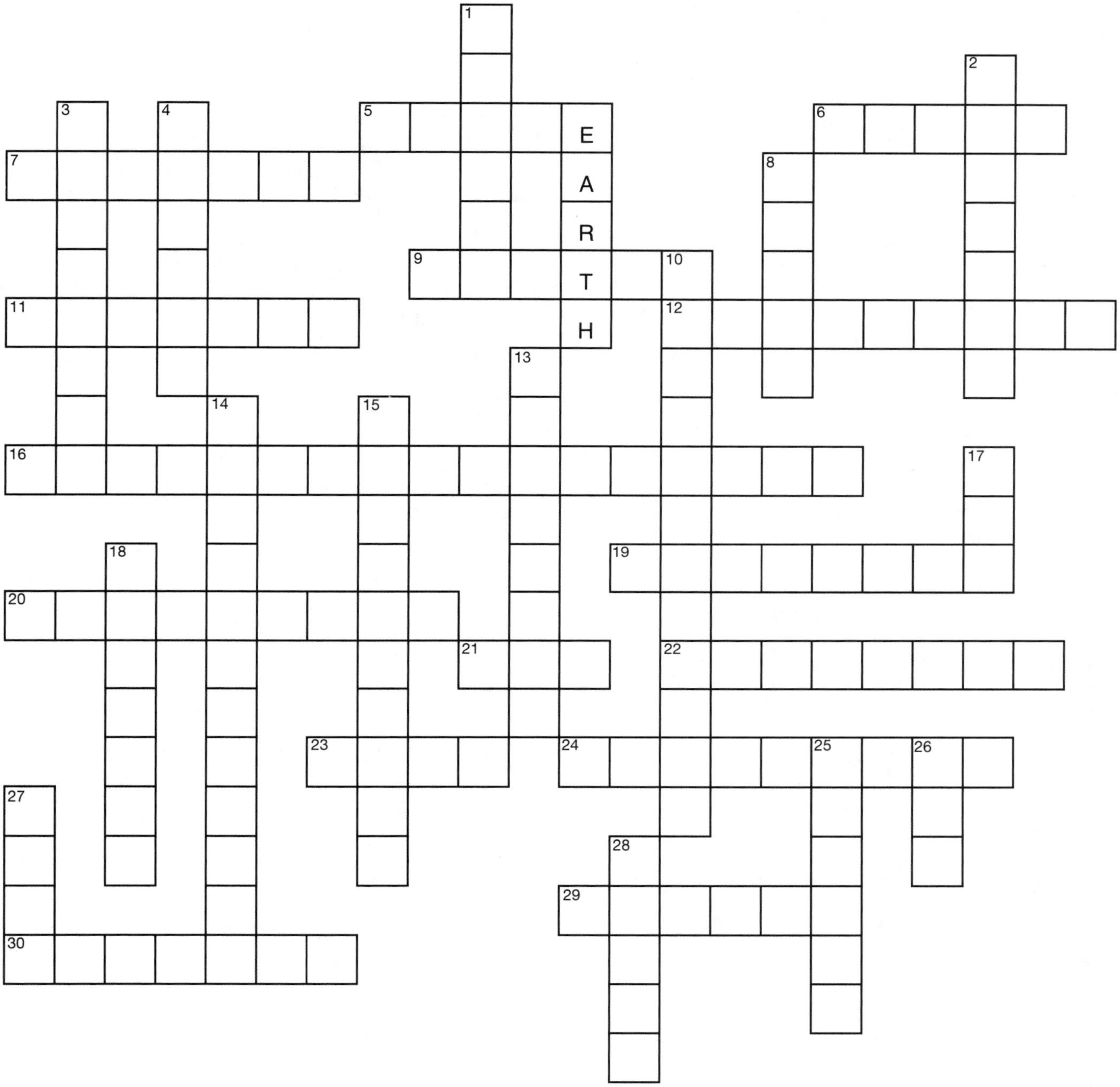
E
A
R
T
H

# 1C Clear Thinking

Did you know that clear thinking is a characteristic of a Christian? In 1 John 4:1 Christians are exhorted to "try the spirits," or to test their teachers. Peter tells Christians to be "ready always to give an answer" (1 Peter 3:15). This investigation is an exercise in clear thinking that will help you to recognize and avoid fallacies in logic.

A fallacy is a mistake in reasoning; it is one type of incorrect argument. Though there are many types of fallacies in reasoning, this exercise will concentrate on just six: hasty generalization, circular reasoning, *ad hominem*, missing the point, appeal to force, and the "pretended-neutrality" fallacy.

## Hasty Generalization Fallacy

This fallacy occurs when a general conclusion is drawn from a small number of cases that are not typical of the whole group.

*Example*: It rained the first three days of July at this resort. It must rain all summer here.

*Example*: Faraday was a Christian. Maxwell, Kelvin, and Boyle were Christians. All leading scientists of bygone days were believers.

Pollsters commit this error when they use a sample that is too small or that is not representative of the whole. Sometimes this is done on purpose by the media or special interest groups in order to influence their followers.

## Circular Reasoning Fallacy

Circular reasoning is assuming what you are trying to prove and using it as support for your argument. This is known as "begging the question."

*Example*: He claims that I am his best friend. It must be true because nobody would lie to his best friend.

*Example*: The only valid way to tell whether a statement is true or false is by the use of logic and reason. I know this is so because it is logical and reasonable.

This fallacy often involves at least two statements, each of which depends on the other for its support.

## *Ad Hominem* Fallacy

This fallacy involves an attack on the *person* supporting the argument rather than on the argument itself. This action fails in its purpose, for it cannot destroy the argument by showing that the arguer has defects in his character or blots on his record. Even the most disreputable

## Goal
Identify fallacies in the following isolated examples.

## Materials
None

person sometimes makes true statements and offers sound arguments. (*Ad hominem* is Latin for "to the man.")

*Example*: Francis Bacon was convicted of accepting bribes while holding a government office. Therefore, we cannot believe anything he wrote about the scientific method.

Sometimes an attack is made on a person's occupation, family connections, or other circumstances that might influence his decision making.

*Example*: His research paper on the chemical composition of certain sedimentary rocks is unreliable because he is an evolutionary atheist.

## Missing the Point Fallacy

This fallacy, sometimes called "irrelevant conclusions," is committed when an argument seemingly leading to one conclusion is directed to a different conclusion.

*Example*: Your Honor, my client is not guilty; because he was under the influence of alcohol when he committed the crime, he was not responsible for his actions.

*Example*: Christianity is the one true religion. Just look at the good that has resulted from the efforts of Christians all over the world.

## Appeal to Force Fallacy

An arguer commits this fallacy when, instead of offering valid reasons to support his conclusion, he threatens severe consequences if his conclusion is not accepted. This fallacy's power to persuade rests in the fact that it instills some form of fear in the listener, either directly or indirectly; the threat may be physical, or it may be of a more subtle nature.

*Example*: There certainly is a Santa Claus. But he does not bring any presents to children who do not believe in him.

*Example*: You need to get saved, or you will not be able to get a job anywhere in this town.

## "Pretended-Neutrality" Fallacy

Scientists, judges, and others who are required to rule on evidence or disagreements between individuals are expected to be unbiased in making their decisions. The decision is supposed to be based only on the merits of the argument. This approach to decision-making assumes that the individual has no presuppositions that affect the decision. Since everyone has presuppositions that affect every decision he makes, people who claim that they are unbiased are committing this fallacy.

*Example*: Religion requires that one accept certain presuppositions (beliefs) by faith. Since science is concerned with what is rational and unbiased, no true scientist can hold to religious beliefs over scientific facts.

## Procedure

Decide which of the types of fallacies discussed above is illustrated by each of the following statements.

1. All swans are white. John showed me what he claimed was a black swan, but I know it could not have been a real swan; it was the wrong color.

   _____

2. You cannot trust his testimony. He is only a high-school student.

   _____

3. Last night my folks made me practice the piano, and tonight they made me do homework. They never want me to have any fun.

   _____

4. Tom has the highest average in the class because he is the best student. He *must* be the best student, or he would not be surpassing all the others with his grades.

   _____

5. Dr. Permian believes that true science can result only from studying natural processes and laws. He thinks that bringing Christian beliefs into the laboratory introduces unscientific biases that will invalidate the experimental results.

   _____

6. Mr. Roberts has accused me of incompetence. But he is the one who was twice demoted and finally fired from his job at Barker Sheet Metal.

   _____

7. Jim Thorpe was an American Indian and one of the world's greatest athletes. Judging by his prowess, I believe all American Indians must be tremendous athletes.

   _____

8. Captain, you will sign this confession, or we will begin shooting your crew members one at a time while you watch.

   _____

9. I put in a fair amount of study on the last two tests, but I still flunked them both. For this test I am going to try not studying at all.

   _____

10. If we let homosexuals force their beliefs on the general population, the rest of us will lose our rights.

    _____

11. Man is a rational being. Therefore, I am sure Mr. Smith will be reasonable about the window you broke in his house.

    _____

Investigation

# 1D Finding Fallacies in an Evolutionary Essay

The author of the following essay uses a number of logical and scientific errors as he develops his erroneous position that evolution is now a certainty. The scientific errors are of two general kinds: lack of observations and misinterpretation of data. (1) *Lack of observations*— Very few fossils that could be interpreted as "missing links" can be found in the fossil record; yet the writer never mentions this. He glosses over the very important fact that the many necessary in-between forms are *not* documented by fossil evidence. (2) *Misinterpretation of data*—The small differences found in different varieties of the same species are assumed by evolutionists to be indefinitely extendible all the way from amoeba to man. Experiments indicate, however, that genetic differences within a kind have definite limits.

## Goal
Identify evolutionary fallacies in an essay.

## Materials
none

## Procedure

In this exercise you will concern yourself with only the *logical* fallacies in the essay. There is at least one example of each of the six types of fallacies described in Investigation 1C. Some are used more than once. Write the name of each fallacy in the margin where it occurs.

*Evolution—An Established Fact*

Those who deny evolution are simply stubborn, inflexible individuals who lack the scientific training necessary to understand its truth. Evolution is just as much a fact of nature as the law of gravity. It is constantly going on around us, but it occurs at such a slow rate that we cannot see it happening. We tend to see only the present biological world—the space and time in which we find ourselves—rather than the long-term evolutionary picture. As the proverb goes, "We can't see the forest for the trees." But regardless of whether we can see it happening, evolution is the force that has brought us to our present high level of development and, barring nuclear catastrophe, will continue to shape our destiny in eternity to come.

Consequently, college students who bypass science courses deprive themselves of the foundation necessary to develop a mature philosophy toward life. Unfortunately, many businessmen, clergymen, artists, musicians, and lawyers suffer from the same deficiency because of the nonscientific nature of their training. This is especially regrettable in the case of clergymen, for they in turn lead entire congregations astray. Unfortunate though this is, it is completely predictable, for their faith binds them in varying degrees to ancient myths that have little relevance to the modern world. Preoccupied with heavenly fantasies, they become unable to think clearly about the real world in which they find themselves.

In today's technological world all knowledgeable people are evolutionists. In fact, we would not be too far afield if we defined a knowledgeable person as one who *does* believe in evolution.

Charles Darwin came up with his theory of evolution in the mid-1800s. He was a scientifically minded man who put aside his religious training in order to objectively consider the facts uncovered by observation. Darwin was interested in the distinctions, or differences, between species and the relationship between those distinctions and the geographic areas in which each type of species lived. In other words, he wondered why different but very similar species could be found living on one continent or in one hemisphere. For example, he observed three distinct types of rodents—North American, South American, and European. Yet their general similarities convinced Darwin that they must have descended from a common ancestor. In addition, he noted that the plants and animals on oceanic islands generally resembled the plants and animals of the nearest continents, but with certain slight differences. Thus, he became convinced that these minor differences represented random changes that had occurred in nature and had become established in the general population of each type of species through the workings of heredity. He gave up his earlier view that all varieties had existed exactly as they were from the very beginning. By projecting these slight changes to hundreds of millions of years, he reasoned that not only whole new species but also new genera, families, and even phyla could be produced. In fact, all living forms could, in principle, be traced to a small number of direct ancestors—or even to a single primeval life form. Darwin was unable to explain exactly what caused the changes to occur, and this problem has defied full explanation even to this day. But in spite of continuing disagreement as to _how_ those changes occurred, no informed person now denies that these changes have in fact taken place.

We see many varied results of evolution on every hand. The towering grandeur of a California redwood, the graceful flight of a red-tailed hawk, the skilled hand of a violinist or surgeon—all of these testify to the great power and flexibility of evolutionary processes. Evolution has tackled a host of challenging engineering problems and solved them with remarkable ingenuity.

Though there are still many unanswered questions concerning the specific details of the evolutionary process, we can construct a broad outline of what took place by studying fossils in the sedimentary rock layers of the earth's crust. Invariably, the oldest rock layers are found to contain the most primitive (earliest and simplest) plants and animals. We can actually date the rocks by the types of fossils they contain. Combining and interpreting the facts obtained from the study of these fossils enables us to construct a comprehensive "road map" giving the essential landmarks in the ancestry of each present-day form of life. The body of knowledge thus obtained is unassailable—it cannot be denied or disproved. Anyone who questions the fact of evolution simply demonstrates his own ignorance. It is especially clear that any scientist who fails to uphold the essential correctness of evolution is incompetent and should be released from his post. Similarly, it follows that any student in a science course who refuses to accept the truth of this important doctrine should receive a failing grade.

# 2 THE EARTH'S MOTIONS

## 2A Geocentric and Heliocentric Theories

### PART 1

*Directions*: Read each of the following phrases carefully and decide which solar-system theory it best describes. Then place the number of the phrase under the proper theory.

1. View held today
2. Earth, Moon, Mercury, Venus, . . .
3. Stationary Earth
4. More simple model
5. Very inaccurate model
6. Atmosphere dragged along by a rotating earth
7. Earth at the center
8. Crystal sphere around the earth called the *deferent*
9. Theory that gained acceptance during the Renaissance
10. Overly complex model
11. Theory accepted during ancient times (BC)
12. Sun, Mercury, Venus, Earth, . . .
13. Planets appear to loop backwards because the earth passes them.
14. More accurate model
15. Model incorporated as theological doctrine by the Roman Catholic Church during the Middle Ages
16. Spinning Earth
17. Sun at the center
18. Planets must move in small circles called *epicycles*.
19. Theory believed by Galileo and Copernicus
20. Theory that is named after its promoter, Ptolemy

**Geocentric**

_____    _____

_____    _____

_____    _____

_____    _____

_____    _____

**Heliocentric**

_____    _____

_____    _____

_____    _____

_____    _____

_____    _____

### PART 2

*Directions*: In the spaces below, define the terms *geocentric* and *heliocentric*.

Geocentric _____

_____

_____

Heliocentric _____

_____

_____

Applications

## 2B  The Earth's Rotation

*Directions*: Use the following statements to choose the right words for the blanks in the puzzle. All of the words pertain to the rotation of the earth.

1. The sun, moon, planets, and stars all __(1)__ in the east.

2. In the Northern Hemisphere, stars appear to move __(2)__ around the North __(3)__.

3. The __(4)__ pendulum was constructed by a French physicist in 1851.

4. The earth's surface is moving faster at the __(5)__ than at the poles.

5. The tendency of moving matter to keep moving in the same direction is __(6)__.

6. If you positioned a Foucault pendulum over the South Pole, you would be able to see the earth turn at a rate of approximately __(7)__ degrees per hour.

7. The __(8)__ prevailing wind __(9)__ occur because the rotating earth deflects the wind.

8. As the earth rotates, it __(10)__ the atmosphere with it.

9. When __(11)__ such as bullets, cannon shells, or missiles take off from the spinning earth, allowances must be made for deflection, or they may miss their target.

10. If the earth did not rotate, we would have half a year of continuous daylight and half of continuous __(12)__.

11. The __(13)__ of the earth is slightly flat at the poles and bulging at the equator.

1. R __ __ __
2. __ __ __ __ __ __ __ __ __ __ O __ __ __ __ __ __
3. __ T __ __
4. __ __ __ __ A __ __ __
5. __ __ __ __ T __ __
6. __ __ __ __ __ I __
7. __ __ __ __ __ __ N
8. __ __ __ G __ __ __ __
9. __ __ __ __ E __ __ __
10. __ __ A __ __
11. __ R __ __ __ __ __ __ __ __ __ __
12. __ __ __ __ T
13. __ H __ __ __

Applications

## 2C Scientists Who Helped Discover the Earth's Motions

*Directions*: Match each man below with the phrases that best describe him. Place the first letter of each name in the proper blank.

| | | |
|---|---|---|
| Aquinas | Galileo | Ptolemy |
| Copernicus | Kepler | Tycho |
| Foucault | Newton | |

_____ 1. Was tried by the Catholic Inquisition for promoting the heliocentric theory, among other reasons

_____ 2. Polish astronomer who formulated the heliocentric theory

_____ 3. Danish nobleman considered to be one of the most accurate astronomical observers

_____ 4. Proved mathematically that the orbits of the planets are elliptical

_____ 5. Played a large role in modifying and improving the heliocentric theory through his careful studies of Tycho's observations

_____ 6. First to see the rings of Saturn

_____ 7. Wrote a book called *New Astronomy*

_____ 8. Author of *The Revolutions*

_____ 9. English scientist who formulated the law of gravity

_____ 10. French physicist who constructed a pendulum that helped to prove that the earth rotates

_____ 11. Italian philosopher who claimed he could harmonize the natural philosophy and thinking of the ancient pagans with Christianity

_____ 12. First to see Jupiter's largest moons

_____ 13. German astronomer who formulated the laws of planetary motion

_____ 14. According to tradition, was inspired by an apple falling from a tree

_____ 15. Hung a 67 m long pendulum inside the Pantheon

_____ 16. Greek philosopher and astronomer who lived in the second century AD and attempted to improve the earth-centered theory of the solar system

Applications

# 2D The Seasons

*Directions*: Fill in the following chart with the correct information. A sample answer for each category has already been given.

| | | | | |
|---|---|---|---|---|
| **Season in the Northern Hemisphere** | | | Spring | |
| **Proper name** | Autumnal equinox | | | |
| **Date (approximate)** | | December 21 | | |
| **Length of days and nights in Northern Hemisphere** | Equal days and nights | | | |
| **Location of sun's perpendicular, noontime rays** | | | Equator | |
| **Position of the sun in the sky for the Northern Hemisphere** | | | | Highest |

## 2E The Foucault Pendulum

Jean Foucault built the first Foucault pendulum in 1851. It was suspended from the ceiling of the Pantheon in Paris, 67 m (220 ft) above the floor. The direction of the swing of the pendulum changed with time. Since the change of the pendulum's swing could occur only if its attachment point was moving around a rotational axis, Mr. Foucault had successfully demonstrated that the earth was turning under the pendulum. This kind of changing motion is called *precession* and can occur in any spinning objects, such as tops, gyros, and vehicle wheels.

### Setting Up

1. Place the face of the 24-hour clock on the swivel surface (called the "turntable") that you have been provided so that the center of the clock is in the center of the turntable. Tape it in place.

2. Extend the tripod legs to their full lengths. Set the tripod on the turntable so that it is as centered as possible.

3. Tie the string to the threaded camera mount on the lower end of the tripod's center post.

4. Tie the mass to the other end of the string so that the mass just clears the dial as it swings. The longer the string the better.

### Procedure and Observations

1. Start the pendulum swinging so that it crosses the 12- and 24-hour marks of the clock face.

2. While the pendulum is swinging, rotate the turntable ¼ turn counterclockwise. What hour marks does the pendulum cross now?

   _____

3. Move the turntable another ¼ turn counterclockwise. What hour marks does the pendulum cross now?

   _____

4. Move the turntable another ¼ turn counterclockwise. What hour marks does the pendulum cross now?

   _____

5. Move the turntable another ¼ turn counterclockwise. What hour marks does the pendulum cross?

   _____

### Goal
Demonstrate the earth's movement that causes precession of a Foucault pendulum

### Materials
camera tripod

turntable (lazy Susan, swivel stool, record player turntable, etc.)

24-hour clock face from page SA17

sewing thread

50 g hooked laboratory mass (or other dense object, such as a large machine nut)

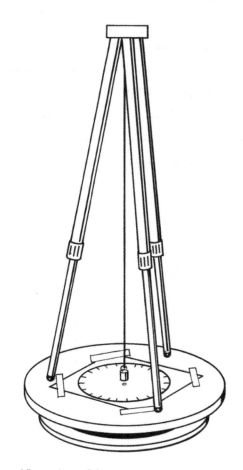

Setup of Foucault pendulum

6. Stop the swinging pendulum and start over again. Repeat the experiment and compare your results. What do you find?

_____

_____

7. Adjust one of the tripod's legs so that the hanging pendulum is as far off to one side of the turntable as possible. Move the clock face so that it is centered under the pendulum.

8. Repeat steps 1–5. What do you find? _____

_____

_____

## Summing Up

1. If a pendulum were swinging directly over the North Pole for a 24-hour period, what would happen?

_____

_____

_____

2. Would the effect be observable in a city on the same latitude as Chicago?

_____

_____

_____

3. What would happen if the pendulum were at the equator? Why?

_____

_____

_____

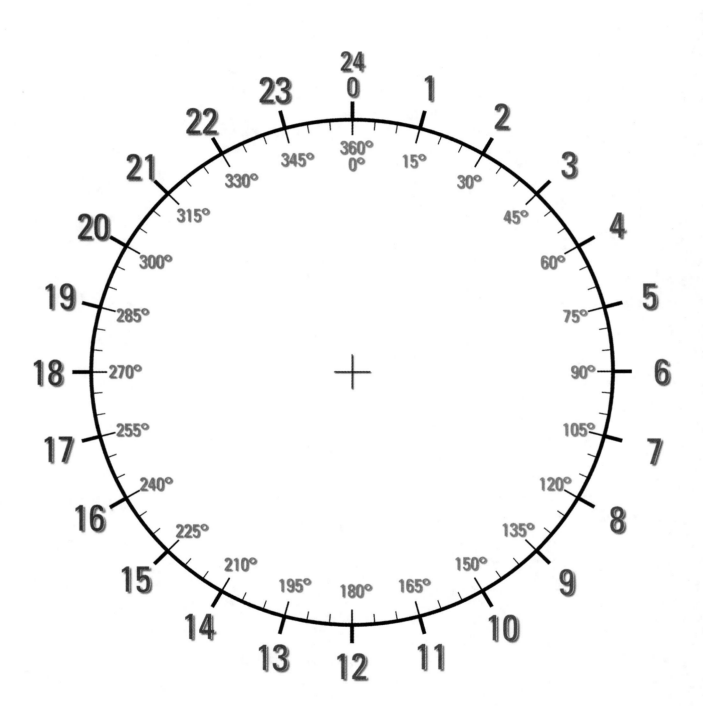

Investigation
# 2F Measuring the Earth

Until the advent of space probes, the earth could not be measured directly. No tape measure would be long enough! However, there are ways to measure the earth indirectly. Eratosthenes, a Greek mathematician and astronomer, was the first to devise a method that yielded a surprisingly accurate answer. While the details of how he obtained his data vary, the following facts are known. On June 21 (the summer solstice) about 225 BC in the Egyptian city of Syene (near present-day Aswan), he observed that the noon sun shone directly down a deep, dry well without casting a shadow. On that day the sun was directly over Syene. A year later on June 21 in Alexandria, a city about 800 km north of Syene, he measured the angle of the shadow that a gnomon cast under a noon sun and found it to be 7.2° from the vertical.

Eratosthenes believed, as did most Greek philosophers at the time, that the earth was a perfect sphere. By setting up a proportion, he calculated the circumference of the earth. We will be using his method to measure the circumference of a desk globe of the earth.

## Procedure and Observations

1. In a darkened room, position the lamp at least 4 m away from the globe. (At this distance the light rays illuminating the globe are nearly parallel.)

2. Slowly move the first stick up and down along a longitude (vertical) line, keeping it perpendicular to the surface of the globe. Stop when it reaches the point where it casts no shadow. Fasten the stick onto the globe at that point with a piece of clay.

3. Verify that the stick is perpendicular to the globe's surface by using the protractor. Place the protractor's straight edge on the globe and position it so that the globe's surface curves away equally on both sides of the point of contact. The stick should align with the 90° mark. Make this check parallel to both the longitude and latitude lines.

### Goal
Use Eratosthenes' method to measure the circumference of a globe.

### Materials
modeling clay

desk globe at least 20 cm in diameter (a large sports ball can be substituted)

300-watt lamp (An overhead projector will work.)

protractor

tape measure (preferably metric)

thin string (5 m)

two sticks 2 mm thick and at least 10 cm long (Flame test splints can be used.)

Eratosthenes (ehr uh TAHS thuh NEEZ) (276–194 BC)

4. After the completion of Step 3, do not allow the globe to move for the remaining steps.

5. Measure a distance of exactly 5 cm directly north from the base of the first stick. Using clay, fasten the second stick at that point. Check to see that the second stick is perpendicular to the globe's surface.

6. The second stick should be casting a shadow on the globe. Fasten the string down with clay at the very tip of the shadow. Carefully, without pushing over the second stick, draw the string taut between the end of the shadow and the top of the second stick.

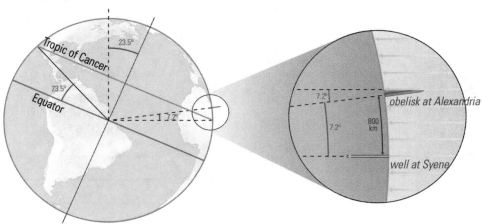

7. Measure the angle between the second stick and the string, making sure that the string passes over the tip of the stick. You may want someone to hold the string in place and the stick perpendicular to the globe as you do this. Repeat the procedure to check the accuracy of your measurement. After three trials, find the average value of angle $X$ and write it in the blank.

**Shadow Angle**

Trial 1 _____

Trial 2 _____

Trial 3 _____

Average_____

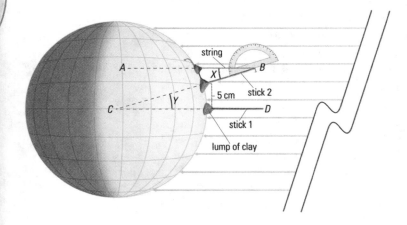

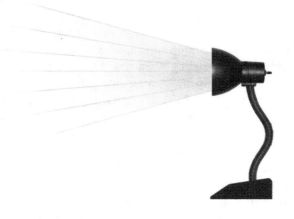

## Summing Up

1. Refer to the diagram above. Lines $AB$ and $CD$ are parallel because we assume that the light rays from the lamp are parallel. Angle $X$ and angle $Y$ are called alternate interior angles and are formed when a line, such as $CB$, crosses parallel lines. From geometry, we know that alternate interior angles are equal. Therefore,

   angle $X$ = angle $Y$.

   The 5 cm distance between the sticks is the part of the circumference that corresponds to angle $Y$. Keeping in mind that a full circumference contains 360°, you can set up the following proportion:

   $$\frac{\text{circumference}}{5 \text{ cm}} = \frac{360°}{\text{angle } Y}$$

   Remembering that angle $Y$ = angle $X$, solve for the circumference of the globe. The circumference is

   _____.

2. Now, to check the accuracy of the results of your experiment, use the tape measure to measure the actual circumference of the globe. Make sure that you measure along a continuous circle of longitude. The globe measures

   _____.

   (*Note*: If a tape measure is not available, wrap a string once around the globe's equator; then measure the length of the string.)

3. Find the percent error of your results. The experimental value is the one calculated in Step 1.

   percent error =

   $$\frac{(\text{experimental value} - \text{actual value})}{\text{actual value}} \times 100\%$$

   percent error = _____

   What are some possible sources of error in Eratosthenes' method?

   _____

   _____

   _____

   _____

   _____

4. Using Eratosthenes' angle for $X$, and substituting his distance for 5 cm, calculate the polar circumference of the earth in kilometers using the proportion in Step 1.

   Circumference = _____

5. The accepted polar circumference is 39,940 km. Why is this different from the equatorial circumference of 40,075 km?

   _____

   _____

   _____

   _____

Investigation

## 2G Time of Day: Ancient and Modern

### PART 1: ANCIENT

In the Bible the word *day* is used in at least two different ways. As a twenty-four-hour period (one rotation of the earth on its axis), *day* appears in such references as Genesis 1:5, in which God declares that "the evening and the morning were the first day." The Jewish day extended from sunset to sunset; the Roman day, from midnight to midnight. As the period from sunrise to sunset (twelve hours), *day* is defined by our Lord Himself: "*Jesus answered, Are there not twelve hours in the day? If any man walk in the day, he stumbleth not, because he seeth the light of this world*" (John 11:9). Interestingly, this is the first direct mention of the twelve-hour daylight period in the Bible. The day was not divided into numbered hours in Old Testament times. But beginning in the book of Matthew, there are references to "the third hour of the day," "the sixth hour of the day," and so forth.

### Goals

Gain familiarity with timekeeping in Bible times.

Relate times given in Scripture to modern clock times.

### Materials:

None

| | | | | | |
|---|---|---|---|---|---|
| **Jewish Day** | | | | | |
| **Roman Day** | | | | | |

Sunset  Midnight  Sunrise  Noon  Sunset  Midnight

Even though the length of the daylight period varies with the latitude of the observer and the time of year, it can be assumed that sunrise in the Scriptures means 6:00 a.m. and sunset means 6:00 p.m. and that the hours have the same length as modern hours.

### Procedure

Give the modern clock time for each biblical daylight time listed. Be sure to indicate whether it is a.m., p.m., or noon. (*Hint*: Begin at 6:00 a.m. and count forward the given number of hours. For example, the fourth hour of the day would be 10:00 a.m.)

| Reference | Biblical daylight time | Modern equivalent |
|---|---|---|
| 1. Matthew 20:3 | third hour of the day | |
| 2. Matthew 20:6 | eleventh hour of the day | |
| 3. Mark 15:33 | sixth hour of the day | |
| 4. Mark 15:34 | ninth hour of the day | |
| 5. John 1:39 | tenth hour of the day | |
| 6. John 4:6 | sixth hour of the day | |
| 7. John 4:52 | seventh hour of the day | |
| 8. Acts 2:15 | third hour of the day | |
| 9. Acts 3:1 | ninth hour of the day | |
| 10. Acts 10:9 | sixth hour of the day | |

## Observations

Note that the examples given are all from the New Testament. In Old Testament times, only terms such as *sunrise, morning, noon, heat of the day, cool of the day, sunset,* and *evening* were used. Also note that this exercise has dealt with only the daylight hours. The night, from 6:00 p.m. to 6:00 a.m., was divided into watches. In New Testament times there were four watches, each three hours in length. The night was also subdivided into hours. Acts 23:23 refers to "the third hour of the night," corresponding roughly to 9:00 p.m.

## PART 2: MODERN

Since the earth turns on its axis 15° per hour, astronomers and geographers have chosen to divide the earth into time zones that are each 15 degrees of longitude wide.

All geographical points within a given zone share the same time. The 15° width of each zone allows the 360° of the globe to be evenly divided into twenty-four time zones. The system is centered on the prime meridian, the line of longitude running through Greenwich, England (the dashed line in the figure to the right). In general, the time in each zone is one hour later than the time zone to its west. The one exception to this rule occurs at the International Date Line (in the drawing, the dashed line located on the side of the earth farthest from the prime meridian). The date line splits the time zone into two 7½° zones. Both sides of the date line have the same clock time but different dates. To the east of the date line, the date is one day earlier than it is to the west of the date line. Thus, it would be possible to celebrate your birthday on two consecutive days if you crossed the line in a ship headed from west to east. Conversely, you could miss it altogether if you crossed the line from east to west at midnight.

The contiguous United States are divided into four time zones. From west to east these are Pacific, mountain, central, and eastern standard time. Notice that the boundaries of the zones are somewhat irregular in the diagram on the next page. State boundary lines are often used so that different parts of a state are not in different time zones.

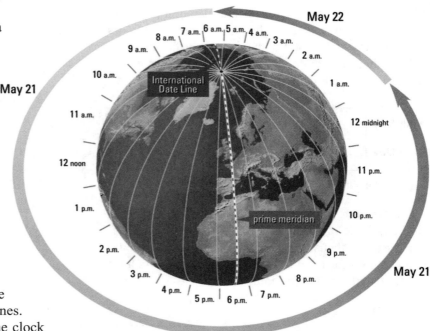

## Procedure and Observations

1. The first five questions concern the contiguous United States. Since the earth rotates from west to east, people in the eastern time zone are the first to experience a given time. Those in the central time zone experience it an hour later; those in the mountain time zone, two hours later; and those in the Pacific time zone, three hours later. Using this information, answer the following questions.

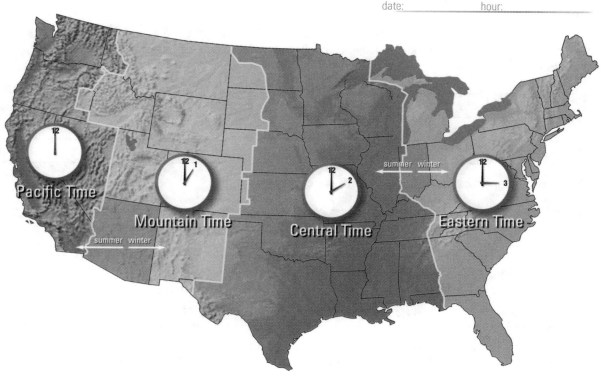

a. What time is it in New York City (eastern time) when it is 6:00 a.m. in Los Angeles (Pacific time)?

_____

b. What time is it in Chicago (central time) when it is 12:00 midnight in New York City (eastern time)?

_____

c. Is it possible for it to be Friday on the East Coast while it is Thursday on the West Coast?

_____

d. When it is 1:00 p.m. in New York City (eastern time), what time is it in Denver (mountain time)?

_____

e. When it is 7:00 p.m. in San Francisco (Pacific time), what time is it in New Orleans (central time)?

_____

2. The next questions concern timekeeping in a more general sense. Recalling that the earth rotates from west to east, you can understand the fact that England is five hours ahead of eastern standard time and eight hours ahead of Pacific standard time. The time in England has a special significance. Called Greenwich mean time (GMT), it is standard time everywhere in the world. Greenwich time is given on a twenty-four-hour basis and does not use a.m.

and p.m. The morning hours run from zero to twelve; the afternoon and evening hours run from twelve to twenty-four. Four digits are always used, the first two for the hour, the last two for the minutes past the hour. Thus, 10:30 a.m. is written 1030 GMT, and so on. For the morning hours before 10:00 a.m., a zero occupies the first digit. For example, 8:30 a.m. is 0830 GMT.

Answer the following questions, keeping in mind the fact that Greenwich is five hours ahead of eastern standard time.

a. What is eastern time when the time in England is 1500 GMT?

_____

b. What is the Greenwich mean time when it is 2:00 a.m. in Boston (eastern time)?

_____

c. What time is it in Sacramento (Pacific time) when the time in England is 2230 GMT?

_____

d. What is the Greenwich mean time when it is 7:00 a.m. in New Orleans (central time)?

_____

e. What is the time in Denver (mountain time) when the time in England is 1800 GMT?

_____

## Summing Up

1. Give two meanings of the word *day* in the Bible, both of them referring to a definite unit of time. What is the significance of the word *day* when referring to Creation in Genesis 1?

   _____

   _____

   _____

   _____

2. In New Testament times, how many watches were there in a night?

   _____

3. What is the modern equivalent of the fourth watch?

   _____

4. Why was a width of 15° chosen for the time zones?

   _____

   _____

5. Given that the International Date Line runs north and south through the Pacific Ocean, could it possibly be Wednesday in Japan while it is still Tuesday in the United States?

   _____

Investigation

# 2H The Solar Day vs. the Sidereal Day

Each day the sun sets at a slightly different time due to the fact that the earth travels in its orbit around the sun in addition to rotating on its axis. You can measure the time it takes the earth to rotate once either in reference to the sun or in reference to the stars. If you measure the period of the earth's rotation with respect to the sun, you are determining the length of a *solar* day. If you measure it with respect to the stars (or some fixed point in space), however, you are determining the length of a *sidereal* day. A mean solar day (24:00 h) is about four minutes longer than a sidereal day. In this investigation you will determine the length of a sidereal day.

## Goal
Demonstrate that a solar day is longer than a sidereal day.

## Materials/Requirements
long wooden stakes (1 to 2 m long)
quartz clock or watch
push pin (optional)
two consecutive clear nights
telescope with a rigid mount (optional)

## Procedure and Observations

1. Measure the length of a sidereal day by lining up a star (be careful not to use a planet) with two sighting marks. Pound one stake into the ground, and then move the second stake until the two stakes are in line with the star. If possible, pound the second stake far enough into the ground (or cut it shorter) so that the star can be seen by sighting across the tops of the two stakes. Alternatively, look through a window until you see a star right at the edge of a wall, telephone pole, or some other distant fixed object. Then you can stick a pin into a window sash (with your parent's permission) to use for your second sighting mark.

2. To use the sighting marks, it is best to position yourself several meters from the near stake or pin so that both marks are easily in focus.

3. Using a clock or watch, record the times on two successive nights that a star lines up with your two markers. Be sure that it is the same star each night. The length of time from your first clock reading to your second clock reading is one sidereal day.

    a. How long is your measured sidereal day?

    _____

    _____

    b. Is it longer or shorter than a solar day?

    _____

    How much longer or shorter is it?

    _____

4. If you have a telescope with a rigid mount, you can perform this demonstration more accurately. Set the telescope up to sight through a window or place it on a protected porch. Choose a distinctive bright star and adjust the telescope mount until the star is exactly in the middle of the field of view. Lock the mount and note the time by an accurate watch. Leave the telescope undisturbed until the next sighting.

5. The next day, note the time when the same star appears exactly in the same place in the field of view.

# 3 THE GLORY OF THE STARS

Applications

## 3A Early Astronomical Devices

*Directions*: Below is a series of diagrams of some early astronomical devices. In the spaces provided, give the name of each device and its use.

**Name of Device**          **Use of Device**

1. _____     1. _____
                          _____
                          _____
                          _____

2. _____     2. _____
                          _____
                          _____
                          _____

3. _____     3. _____
                          _____
                          _____
                          _____

4. _____     4. _____
                          _____
                          _____
                          _____

5. _____     5. _____
                          _____
                          _____
                          _____

Applications

# 3B Telescopes

## PART 1: TYPES OF TELESCOPES

*Directions*: Read each of the following statements and decide which type of telescope is being described. Then indicate your answers by writing the proper words in the blanks provided.

> refractor      reflector      composite      radio

_____ 1. Uses both mirrors and an objective lens

_____ 2. Uses only lenses to gather light

_____ 3. Uses only mirrors to gather light

_____ 4. Does not use mirrors or lenses to gather light

_____ 5. Galileo was the first to use a telescope of this form for astronomy.

_____ 6. Collects waves with a concave disk antenna

_____ 7. The Cassegrainian telescope is of this form.

_____ 8. Has the greatest problem with chromatic aberration

_____ 9. Name comes from the word meaning "to bend or break"

_____ 10. Form exemplified by the Schmidt-Cassegrainian telescope

_____ 11. Form exemplified by the Keck telescopes

_____ 12. Can be used as a radar to explore nearby space objects

_____ 13. The form first developed by Newton

## PART 2: OPTICAL TELESCOPES

*Directions*: Study the figures below and decide which type of telescope is shown. Then indicate your answers by writing the proper words in the blanks provided.

> refractor      Newtonian reflector      composite      Cassegrainian reflector

14. _____

16. _____

15. _____

17. _____

Applications
# 3C Areas in the Sky

## PART 1: THE CONSTELLATIONS

*Directions*: Read the following statements. In the spaces provided, write *True* if the statement is true and *False* if the statement is false.

_____ 1. For modern astronomers, a constellation is an area of the sky, not a picture or image formed by a group of stars.

_____ 2. Boundaries of modern constellations are formed from line segments parallel to celestial latitude and longitude.

_____ 3. Modern astronomers followed the outlines of ancient constellations in forming the present constellations.

_____ 4. The Greek astronomer Hipparchus is given credit for developing an orderly system for identifying stars within a constellation.

_____ 5. Modern astronomers use numbers and Greek or Roman letters to identify stars in a constellation.

_____ 6. Bayer assigned Greek letters to the most prominent stars, usually beginning with alpha for the brightest, beta for the second brightest, and so on.

_____ 7. Following the Greek letter assigned to a star, Bayer attached the possessive form of the constellation's name.

_____ 8. Astronomers never use proper names to identify stars.

_____ 9. Sometimes stars of a constellation are named in order as they appear in the pattern instead of by brightness.

_____ 10. Scientists have agreed on the boundaries of eighty-eight constellations.

## PART 2: THE BIG DIPPER

*Directions*: Label the stars of the Big Dipper—list the proper name first, then the Greek name. Dubhe is labeled for you.

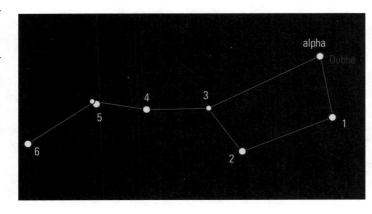

| Proper Name | Greek Name |
|---|---|
| Dubhe | Alpha |
| 1. _____ | _____ |
| 2. _____ | _____ |
| 3. _____ | _____ |
| 4. _____ | _____ |
| 5. _____ | _____ |
| 6. _____ | _____ |

Applications

# 3D Astronomical Geography

## PART 1: STAR CHART

Study the star chart below carefully. Notice that the hours for right ascension are printed at the top and bottom of the chart and are read from right to left. Right ascension is read from right to left because this view of the stars is from the inside of the "celestial sphere." (*Note*: This star chart does not cover the entire sky.) Degrees of declination are printed on the right and left margins.

*Directions*: Locate the following stars, using the star chart below. As you find each one, circle the appropriate star and write its name to the side of it.

| | | |
|---|---|---|
| Altair: | RA: 19 h 48 m; DEC +8.44° | Fomalhaut: RA: 22 h 55 m; DEC –29.53° |
| Arcturus: | RA: 14 h 13 m; DEC +19.27° | Spica: RA: 13 h 23 m; DEC –10.54° |
| Deneb: | RA: 20 h 40 m; DEC +45.06° | Vega: RA: 18 h 35 m; DEC +38.44° |

1. Each of the six stars is among the twenty brightest stars seen from the earth. Look at the stars you have located and compare them to other stars on the chart. What do you think the size of each star dot on the chart represents?

   _____

   _____

2. The stars Arcturus and Vega are among the five brightest stars. If Vega is +0.04 and Arcturus is –0.06, which one is brighter? Why?

   _____

   _____

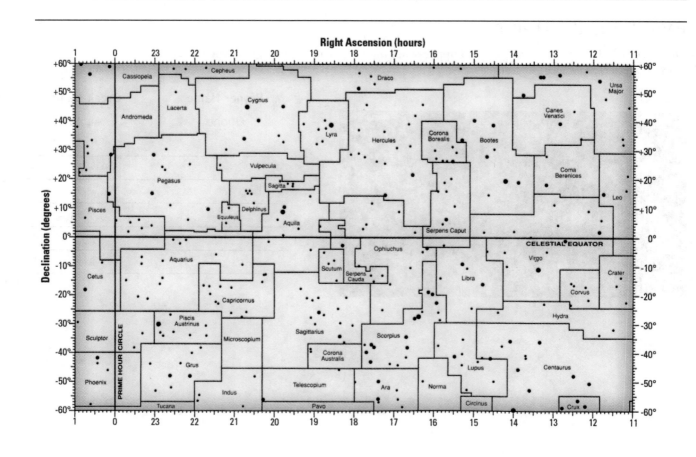

# PART 2: ASTRONOMICAL COORDINATES

*Directions*: Label the directional lines illustrated by each drawing.

**Earth**

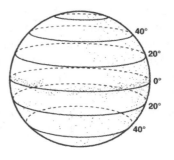

**Sky**

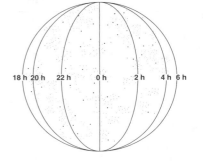

1.  Horizontal lines: _____

2.  Beginning line, 0°: _____

3.  Horizontal lines: _____

4.  Beginning line, 0°: _____

**Earth**

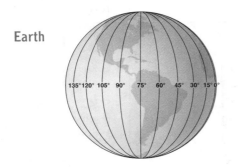

**Sky**

5.  Vertical lines: _____

6.  Beginning line, 0°: _____

7.  Vertical lines: _____

8.  Beginning line, 0 h: _____

# PART 3: CELESTIAL SPHERE

*Directions*: To the right are several views of the sky as a celestial sphere with the earth at the center. Answer the following questions, using the right ascension and declination markings on each sphere.

1.  Give the right ascension and declination for star A:

    RA _____        DEC _____

2.  Give the right ascension and declination for star B:

    RA _____        DEC _____

For questions 3–5 match the following stars and their locations with the letters marked on the celestial sphere.

_____ 3.  Rigel: RA 5 h; DEC –8°

_____ 4.  Procyon: RA 7 h; DEC +5°

_____ 5.  Betelgeuse: RA 6 h; DEC +7°

6.  The location of Deneb is RA 20 h; DEC +45°. Plot this star on the sphere to the right.

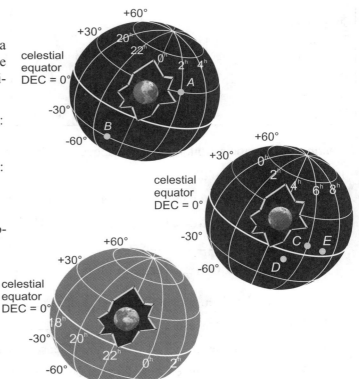

Applications

# 3E Star Characteristics

The following table of the twenty brightest stars will be used in this exercise. Next to the proper name of the star is its Bayer's designation given by a Greek letter and the abbreviation of the constellation where it is found. The star's right ascension (RA) is given in hours and minutes, and its declination (DEC) is given in degrees. A star's visual magnitude ($m_v$) is a measure of its apparent brightness. The actual amount of light a star emits is given by its absolute magnitude (*M*). The distance to a star is reported in light-years (ly). The star's proper motion among other stars is given in seconds per year (a second of angle is $\frac{1}{3600}$ of 1 degree). Radial motion of a star is given in kilometers per second (km/s) and is positive if the star is moving toward the earth, negative if it is moving away from the earth.

## THE TWENTY BRIGHTEST STARS

| Star | RA | | DEC (°) | $m_v$ | M | Distance (ly) | Proper motion (s/y) | Radial motion (km/s) |
|---|---|---|---|---|---|---|---|---|
| | (h) | (min) | | | | | | |
| Sirius (α CMa) | 6 | 45 | −16.7 | −1.50 | +1.41 | 8.5 | 1.324 | −8 |
| Canopus (α Car) | 6 | 24 | −52.7 | −0.73 | −4.7 | 98.1 | 0.034 | +21 |
| Arcturus (α Boo) | 14 | 16 | +19.2 | +0.00 | −0.2 | 35.9 | 2.281 | −5 |
| Rigel Kentaurus (α Cen) | 14 | 40 | −60.8 | +0.01 | +4.3 | 4.4 | 3.678 | −25 |
| Vega (α Lyr) | 18 | 37 | +38.8 | +0.04 | +0.5 | 26.1 | 0.348 | −14 |
| Capella (α Aur) | 5 | 17 | +46.0 | +0.05 | −0.6 | 50.0 | 0.430 | +30 |
| Rigel (β Ori) | 5 | 15 | −8.2 | +0.18 | −7.0 | 599.8 | 0.004 | +21 |
| Procyon (α CMi) | 7 | 39 | +5.2 | +0.34 | +2.65 | 11.4 | 1.248 | −3 |
| Betelgeuse (α Ori) | 5 | 55 | +7.4 | +0.41 | −6.0 | 599.8 | 0.028 | +21 |
| Archernar (α Eri) | 1 | 38 | −57.2 | +0.47 | −2.2 | 64.9 | 0.108 | +16 |
| Hadar (β Cen) | 13 | 4 | −60.4 | +0.61 | −5.0 | 299.9 | 0.030 | +6 |
| Altair (α AqL) | 19 | 51 | +8.7 | +0.77 | +2.3 | 16.6 | 0.662 | −26 |
| Aldebaran (α Tau) | 4 | 36 | +16.5 | +0.86 | −0.7 | 52.2 | 0.200 | +54 |
| Antares (α Sco) | 16 | 29 | −26.4 | +0.90 | −4.7 | 419.8 | 0.024 | −3 |
| Spica (α Vir) | 13 | 25 | −11.2 | +0.98 | −3.4 | 273.8 | 0.054 | +1 |
| Pollux (β Gem) | 7 | 45 | +28.0 | +1.15 | +0.95 | 36.8 | 0.629 | +3 |
| Fomalhaut (α PsA) | 22 | 58 | −29.6 | +1.18 | +1.9 | 22.5 | 0.373 | +7 |
| Mimosa (β Cru) | 12 | 48 | −59.7 | +1.24 | −4.7 | 500.0 | 0.042 | +16 |
| Deneb (α Cyg) | 20 | 41 | +45.3 | +1.26 | −7.3 | 1399.7 | 0.005 | −5 |
| Acrux (α Cru) | 12 | 27 | −63.1 | +1.33 | −3.5 | 389.8 | 0.030 | −11 |

*Directions*: Study the astronomical table above in order to answer the following questions.

1. What designation did Bayer give to the star Altair? _____

2. What are the visual magnitudes for the following stars?

   Rigel Kentaurus (α Cen) _____     Hadar (β Cen) _____

   Rigel (β Ori) _____     Mimosa (β Cru) _____

   Betelguese (α Ori) _____     Acrux (α Cru) _____

   a. Which is brighter, α or β Centauri? _____

   b. Which is brighter, α or β Crucis? _____

   c. Which is brighter, Rigel (β Ori) or Betelgeuse (α Ori)? _____

   d. Did Bayer always give the α designation to the brightest star in the constellation?

   _____

3. Which star from the chart appears brightest?

_____

   a. What is its apparent magnitude? _____

   b. What is its absolute magnitude? _____

   c. How far away is it? _____

4. Which star is brighter, Arcturus or Pollux?

_____

   a. What is the absolute magnitude of Arcturus?

_____

     of Pollux? _____

   b. How far away is Arcturus? _____

     Pollux? _____

   c. Why does Arcturus appear so much brighter than Pollux?

_____

_____

5. Which star appears brighter, Canopus or Antares?

_____

   a. What is the absolute magnitude of Canopus?

_____

     of Antares? _____

   b. How far away is Canopus? _____

     Antares? _____

   c. Why does Canopus appear brighter than Antares?

_____

_____

6. Deneb has an absolute magnitude of −7.3, greatest of the twenty brightest stars. Why is Deneb only the nineteenth brightest star?

_____

_____

7. Rigel Kentaurus (α Centauri) has an absolute magnitude of +4.3, emitting the least amount of light of the twenty brightest stars. Why does it appear to be the fourth brightest star?

_____

_____

8. Which of these twenty stars shows the greatest proper motion?

_____

9. Is Aldebaran moving toward or away from us?

_____

10. Is Altair moving toward or away from us?

_____

Applications

## 3F Types of Galaxies and Nebulae

*Directions*: Below are photographs and renderings of various categories of galaxies and nebulae. In the spaces provided, (a) identify the astronomical object as a galaxy, star cluster, or nebula, and (b) give its classification from the list below. Each term is used at least once.

| Galaxies: | irregular | spiral | barred spiral | elliptical |
|---|---|---|---|---|
| Nebulae: | bright | dark | planetary | |
| Star clusters: | open | globular | | |

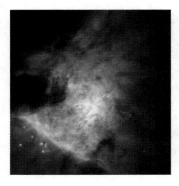

1. a. _____

   b. _____

2. a. _____

   b. _____

| | | | |
|---|---|---|---|
| Galaxies: | irregular | spiral | barred spiral | elliptical |
| Nebulae: | bright | dark | planetary |
| Star clusters: | open | globular |

6. a. _____

   b. _____

3. a. _____

   b. _____

7. a. _____

   b. _____

4. a. _____

   b. _____

8. a. _____

   b. _____

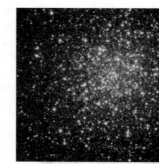

5. a. _____

   b. _____

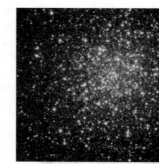

9. a. _____

   b. _____

Investigation

# 3G Curved Lenses and Mirrors

Both refraction and reflection can be used in telescopes to produce and magnify images. In this investigation you will observe characteristics of images produced by lenses and curved mirrors.

## Procedure

## PART 1: REFRACTION IMAGES

1.  Record the focal length of the lens.

    _____

2.  Set up the sheet of card stock as a screen and position the candle and lens as shown. Darken the room. The candle and screen must be well over four focal lengths apart. Measure this distance with the meter stick.

## Goals
Observe images made by lenses.
Observe images made by a curved mirror.

## Materials
candle and matches
two convex lenses (hand lenses) with known focal lengths
concave mirror with a known focal length
white card stock
meter stick or metric tape measure

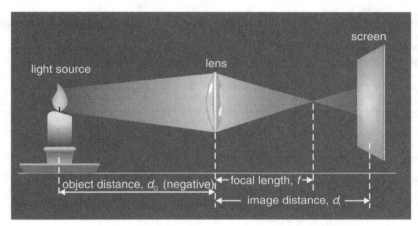

3.  Position the lens a little more than two focal lengths from the candle. Focus the image of the candle flame on the screen by slowly moving the screen back and forth until the image is focused. (The screen should be between one and two focal lengths from the lens.) When the image is in focus, answer the following questions.

    a.  Does the image of the flame appear bright or dim?

        _____

    b.  Is the image upright or inverted? _____

    c.  Is the image smaller or larger than the flame?

        _____

    d.  A lens in this position shows its light-gathering properties. Which lens in a refractor telescope gathers the light?

        _____

4.  Now look at the flame through the lens while holding the lens less than one focal length from the flame.

    a.  Is the image of the flame magnified or reduced?

        _____

    b.  Is the image of the flame upright or inverted?

        _____

    c.  Which lens in a refractor telescope magnifies the image?

        _____

5.  Using the lenses, make a telescope by holding one lens close to your eye inside its focal length and holding the other lens at an arm's distance. Move the lens toward you to focus on a distant object. This is essentially a refractor telescope without a tube.

## PART 2: REFLECTION IMAGES

1. Record the focal length of the mirror.

   _____

2. Set up the card stock as a screen and position the candle and concave mirror as shown. The candle should be more than two focal lengths from the center of the mirror.

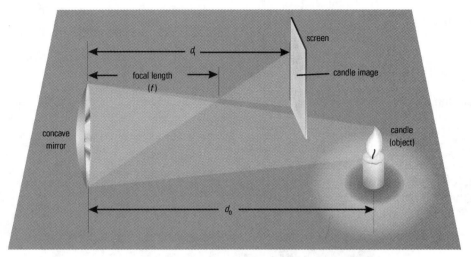

3. To focus the image, move the screen slowly back and forth from one to two focal lengths from the mirror. When the image is in focus, answer the following questions.

   a. Does the image of the flame appear brighter or dimmer than the actual flame?

   _____

   b. Is the image upright or inverted?

   _____

   c. Is the image smaller or larger than the flame?

   _____

   d. What is the function of a curved mirror in a telescope?

   _____

   e. How can the image be magnified?

   _____

Investigation
# 3H Constructing a Paper-Towel-Tube Telescope

A simple refracting telescope is easy to construct. Because of the properties of convex lenses, light from a distant object can be brought to a point and thus intensified. The process is similar in many respects to a funnel that channels a large volume of water into a small opening. An objective lens has the responsibility of "funneling" the light to a smaller area. The eyepiece then magnifies the image produced by the objective lens. In this investigation you will construct a simple telescope. You may use your telescope to observe some of the larger moons of Jupiter and the phases of Venus. You may also be able to better observe some maria and craters on the moon.

## Procedure

1. Cut along a straight line the entire length of one side of one of the tubes. Squeeze the sides of the tube slightly until you can slide it into the other tube. Tape the tube along the cut to create a tube with the smaller diameter.

2. Tape the objective lens around its edges so that it is held firmly inside the end of the larger paper-towel tube. Make four equally spaced cuts about 2 cm long around the edge at the other end of the tube.

3. Tape the eyepiece lens (10× tripod magnifier or other lens) to the end of the smaller paper-towel tube. (Remove the tripod before inserting the magnifier.) You may first have to make slits in the end of the smaller tube to hold the lens.

4. Insert the smaller tube into the larger tube and slip the rubber band around the larger tube at the slits you cut to hold the two tubes snug.

## Goal
Construct a simple telescope.

## Materials
eyepiece lens (A 10× tripod magnifier with the tripod removed works well.)

glue

masking tape

objective lens (A 38 mm diameter × 300 mm focal length works well.)

rubber band

two paper-towel tubes

(optional) ¾ in. × 4 in. × 12 in. piece of wood

(optional) camera tripod

5. Mount the ¾ in. board on your camera tripod. You can tape it or drill a hole and bolt it on, depending on the type of camera tripod you have.

6. Tape the larger tube of your telescope to the board. You are ready to use your telescope.

You may substitute a small lens taped to a ½ in. diameter copper tube about 2 cm long for the tripod magnifier. Hold the eyepiece in the tube with a piece of foam rubber cut to fit into the smaller tube. Alignment of the optical axes of the two lenses is important, so try to line them up carefully.

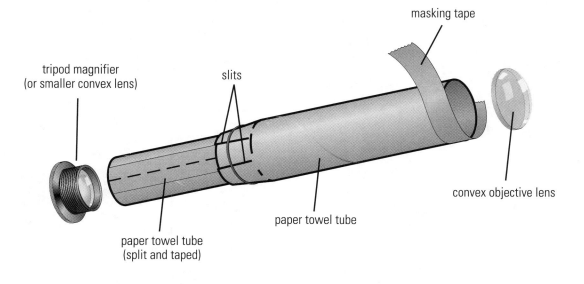

tripod magnifier
(or smaller convex lens)

slits

masking tape

paper towel tube
(split and taped)

paper towel tube

convex objective lens

# 31 Constructing and Using a Constellation Finder

Although seasonal maps of the stars are available, the sky appears different from one part of the season to another and even more so during the different hours of the night. This exercise will provide you with an instrument for determining the location of some of the major constellations in the mid latitudes of the Northern Hemisphere for any day of the year and at any specific time of the night.

In order to simplify things for you, the finder has been abbreviated to show just those constellations mentioned in this textbook. Detailed finders are available from hobby shops and astronomical supply distributors.

## Procedure

1. Spread glue evenly on the back side of the constellation disc and place it on one sheet of construction paper.

2. Remove the frame sheet from page SA41 by cutting along the dashed line. Spread glue evenly on the back of the frame sheet and place it on a second sheet of construction paper.

3. Cut out the constellation disc carefully around the outermost circle.

4. Cut out the shaded areas of the frame sheet, being careful not to cut into any of the borders.

5. Staple the third sheet of construction paper onto the back of the frame sheet. Place staples in the four positions indicated on the frame sheet.

6. Place the constellation disc under the frame sheet so that the outer perimeter of the disc (solid line) registers exactly with the outer circle (not the ellipse) of the frame sheet.

7. Fasten the disc temporarily with tape so that it does not move.

8. Punch a hole through the cross hairs in the center of the disc so that it goes through the disc and the bottom sheet of construction paper.

9. Fasten, using a split tack fastener.

10. Remove the tape supporting the constellation disc and twist the disc until it turns easily. (*Note*: You may want to use masking tape to reinforce the back of the constellation disc and the back of the third piece of construction paper where the fastener comes through to prevent them from tearing.)

## Goals

Construct a constellation finder to use in identifying various constellations throughout the year.

Become proficient in the use of the constellation finder.

## Materials

constellation disc (p. SA43)

frame sheet (p. SA41)

scissors

split tack fastener

stapler

tape

three sheets of construction paper 23 cm × 30 cm

white glue

## Observations

1. Find the time you are observing the sky on the *frame sheet* (e.g., 8:00 p.m.).

2. Turn the *constellation disc* until the observation date printed on the disk (e.g., September 15) is in line with the observation time on the frame sheet.

3. Note the constellations that appear in the elliptical cutout.

4. While facing south, hold the finder over your head so that North on the finder is toward your back. The constellations that appear near the center of the elliptical cutout (not at the fastener) will appear directly overhead as you look into the sky. What constellations appear overhead at 8:00 p.m. on September 15?

_____

5. The outer edges of the ellipse represent the horizon. Constellations located here will be found near the horizon as you look for them in the sky. What constellation is located near the northern horizon at this same date and time?

_____

6. What constellations appear in the south near the horizon?

_____

7. A constellation will be at its zenith (highest point) when it is in line with an imaginary line between North and South on your constellation finder. At what time would Cassiopeia be nearest its zenith on October 10?

   _____

8. On what date would Corona Borealis be at its zenith at 10:00 p.m.? _____

(*Note*: The *midpoint* is a point about halfway between the zenith and the horizon. Use the midpoint when necessary to describe the answers to Questions 9–10.)

9. Where would you look at 9:00 p.m. on January 15 to find

   a. the Great Square of Pegasus? _____

   b. the constellation Taurus? _____

   c. the constellation Leo? _____

10. Where would you look at 9:00 p.m. on September 12 to find

    a. Cassiopeia? _____

    b. the Great Square of Pegasus? _____

    c. Hercules? _____

    d. Cygnus? _____

11. When the star Vega is at the zenith on February 15, is it visible? _____

    Why? _____

12. Fill in the following chart, using your constellation finder.

| Constellation name | Major star(s) | Location | Time | Date |
|---|---|---|---|---|
| Lyra | | zenith | 10:00 p.m. | |
| | Altair | eastern horizon | | Mar. 15 |
| Virgo | | | 8:00 p.m. | Sept. 13 |
| Cygnus | | northwestern horizon | | Jan. 18 |
| Orion | | zenith | midnight | |

13. If the sun is in the center of the constellation Sagittarius on January 10, what time does the sun rise?

    _____ set? _____

    (*Note*: Remember that the sun follows the path of the ecliptic in its trip through the sky.)

14. Observe these constellations sometime within a time period specified by your teacher, and fill in the tables on pages SA41 and SA42.

| Constellation name | Time/date sighted | Location in the sky |
|---|---|---|
| 1. | | |
| 2. | | |
| 3. | | |
| 4. | | |
| 5. | | |
| 6. | | |
| 7. | | |
| 8. | | |
| 9. | | |
| 10. | | |
| 11. | | |
| 12. | | |
| 13. | | |

(continued on next page)

cut

Frame Sheet

STAPLE                                    STAPLE

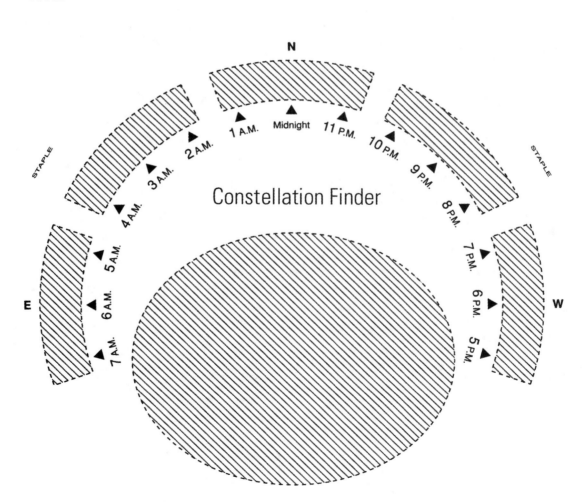

Constellation Finder

| Constellation name | Time/date sighted | Location in the sky |
|---|---|---|
| 14. | | |
| 15. | | |
| 16. | | |
| 17. | | |
| 18. | | |
| 19. | | |
| 20. | | |
| 21. | | |
| 22. | | |
| 23. | | |
| 24. | | |
| 25. | | |

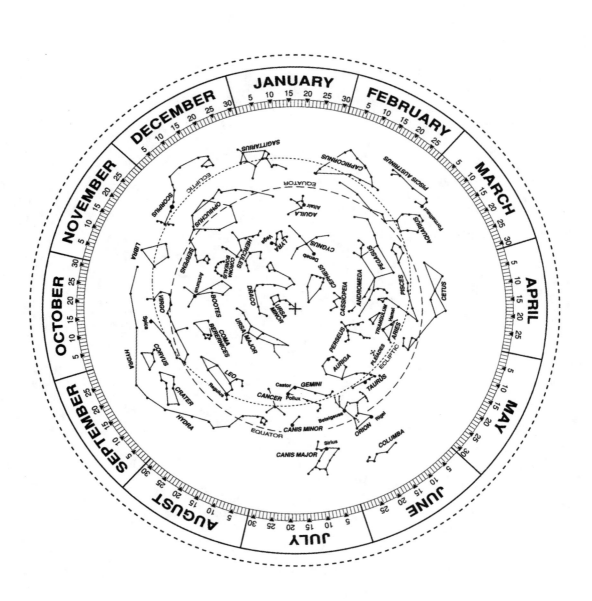

### Investigation
# 3J Measuring Distances to Faraway Objects

It is often impossible to measure the distance to an object directly. Sometimes a river or cliff is between you and the object. Other times the object, such as a star, is too far away. If the object shows any parallax, then its distance can be measured indirectly using a method called triangulation. In this investigation you will use triangulation to find the distance to an object.

To use triangulation, the observer must view the object from two different points. The distance between the points, called the *base line*, must be measured. The longer the base line is, the more accurate your results will be. Two angles also must be measured—the angles between the base line and the line of sight to the object from each endpoint.

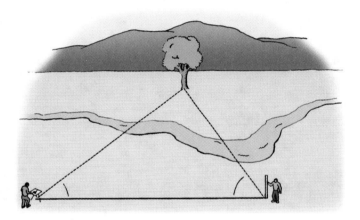

Using these three measurements, the distance from the base line to the object can be calculated mathematically. In this investigation you will construct a triangle to scale to determine the distance using a proportion.

## Procedure and observations

1. Tape the protractor onto a piece of corrugated cardboard. Stick a pin into the pencil near its point. Stick another pin all the way through the eraser on the pencil, parallel to the first pin, and then through the index hole of the protractor into the cardboard.

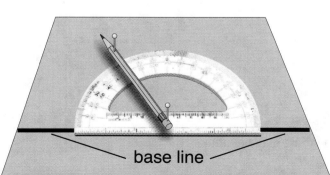

base line

## Goals
Use triangulation to measure a distance.
Gain familiarity with a method of measuring distance to nearby stars.

## Materials
long tape measure
cardboard
string
protractor
table or desk
masking tape
pencil or thin dowel
modeling clay
two straight pins

2. Measure the longest possible base line across the back of the room, leaving room between the base line and the wall to make the sightings. Tape down the string to indicate the base line and mark its ends with masking tape.

3. Make a sighting mark (using tape) on the chalkboard at the front of the room. Position the mark off center about a meter to the left or the right of the center of the base line.

4. Place one table (or desk) over each end of the base line. Make sure that the tables are the same height. Place a piece of masking tape across the top of the table surface to coincide with the base line on the floor. Mark a line across the tape or use the edge of the table to indicate the end of the base line.

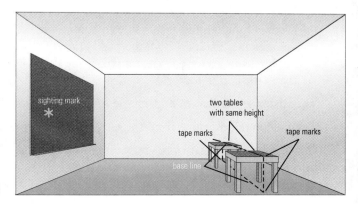

sighting mark

two tables
with same height

tape marks

tape marks

base line

5. After the pieces of tape on the tables are aligned to the base line and marked, measure and record the length of the base line from mark to mark:

_____ m.

6. Position the pivot point of the protractor sighting device directly over the mark at one end of the base line, making sure that its straight edge is aligned to the tape (base line). Without moving the protractor, rotate the pencil so that the two pins on the pencil line up with the mark on the chalkboard. Estimate the angle and record it below. If possible, have two to four other people make the same measurement. Record their results and average all measurements.

7. Repeat Step 6 to obtain the angle at the other end of the base line.

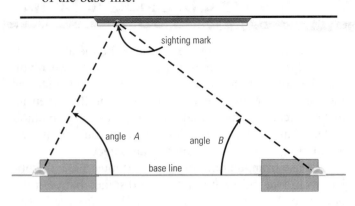

Angle *A*:

_____

_____

_____

_____

Average _____

Angle *B*:

_____

_____

_____

_____

Average _____

## Summing Up

1. The first step in constructing a triangle is to select a scale suitable to the size of the room and the piece of paper. Generally, using a metric ruler for a scale in which 1 cm = 1 m is convenient. For example, if the base line across the back of the room is 20.0 m, the base line on the paper would be 20.0 cm.

   a. Draw a straight line at the bottom of the paper the proper length for the base line.

   b. At the left endpoint, construct an angle the same measure as the (average) left angle from the sighting. Repeat for the right angle.

   c. Extend lines *a* and *b* until they intersect at point *C*.

   d. Draw a perpendicular line from point *C* to the base line. Measure the length of this line in centimeters. This distance is the distance from the base line to the mark on the board in meters. For example, if the distance is 6 cm, the mark is 6 m away.

The distance on the scaled triangle is _____ cm.

The calculated distance from the base line to the mark is _____ m.

(*Note*: This triangle is only an example. The triangle you draw may be quite different.)

2. Use the measuring tape to check your results. The distance measured directly is

   _____ m.

3. Use the formula to calculate the percent error. In the formula the actual value is the distance measured directly. The experimental value is the distance calculated through triangulation.

$$\text{percent error} = \frac{\text{experimental value} - \text{actual value}}{\text{actual value}} \times 100 = \underline{\hspace{1cm}} \%$$

With the invention of powerful telescopes, the parallax for nearby stars became visible and finally measurable. As the diagram shows, the farther the star is from the earth, the smaller its angle of parallax. Very distant stars (more than 325 ly) show no measurable parallax.

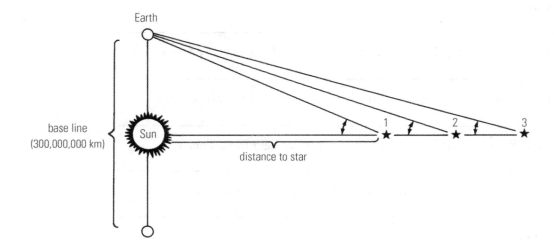

Distance to stars that show parallax can be calculated using triangulation. The base line can be as long as the diameter of the earth's orbit, about 300 million km (186 million mi). The shift in the star's position is measured by sighting the star when the earth is in different positions in its orbit. Parallax cannot be explained by the geocentric theory because the base line is the diameter of the earth's orbit. Parallax not only supports the heliocentric theory but also provides a tool to measure stellar distances.

Investigation
## 3K Calculating the Distance to Proxima Centauri

As you know from reading your text, Proxima Centauri is 4.22 light-years from Earth. And though you may realize that distance is far away, it is sometimes difficult to grasp just how much distance a light-year covers. By calculating the distance to Proxima Centauri, you will gain greater appreciation for the immense distances included in a light-year.

### Goal
Understand better the distance in a light-year.

### Procedure
Light travels 300,000,000 (300 million) meters per second.

1. Multiply the distance light travels per second by 60.0 to figure the distance light travels per minute.

   _____

2. Multiply the answer to Step 1 by 60.0 to figure how far light travels per hour.

   _____

3. Multiply the answer to Step 2 by 24.0 to figure how far light travels per day.

   _____

4. Multiply the answer to Step 3 by 365 to figure how far light travels per year.

   _____

5. Multiply one light-year by 4.22 to figure the distance to Proxima Centauri.

   _____

6. How many kilometers is this?

   _____

7. How many miles is this? (See Appendix A1.)

   _____

### Summing Up
1. Rigel is 600 light-years from Earth. How many kilometers would it be from Earth?

   _____

   How many miles? _____

2. The light-year measurement involves the speed of light. If you go out tonight and see the light coming from Proxima Centauri, when *might* that light have left Proxima Centauri to begin traveling to Earth?

   _____

3. Some evolutionists theorize that solar systems and other objects in the universe can be formed by colliding stars. Based on what you now know about the distances between stars, what is the likelihood of this occurring? Why?

   _____

   _____

name: _____

date: _____ hour: _____

# 4 THE SUN

© 2005 BJU Press. Reproduction prohibited.

Applications

## 4A General Description of the Sun

*Directions*: Below are several groups of words. In each group, three of the four words (or phrases) are related to one another. Draw a line through the unrelated word or phrase and then write a sentence using the remaining words. Your sentence should show how the words are related. You may slightly change the form of the words in your sentence (for example, eye to eyes, fingerprint to fingerprinting).

1. sun / granules / constellation / Hercules

   _____
   _____
   _____

2. moon / 150 million km / sun / earth

   _____
   _____
   _____

3. corona / temperature / photosphere / spicule

   _____
   _____
   _____

4. neutrinos / speed / particles / coronagraph

   _____
   _____
   _____

5. ultraviolet waves / eye / corona / short

   _____
   _____
   _____

6. stars / neutrinos / spectroscope / light

   _____
   _____
   _____

7. constellation / sun / Columba / Mercury

   _____
   _____
   _____

8. speed of light / Milky Way / spiral arms / sun

   _____
   _____
   _____

9. spicules / coronagraph / instrument / artificial eclipse

   _____
   _____
   _____

10. umbra / distance / wavelength / crest

    _____
    _____
    _____

11. infrared waves / penumbra / long / eye

    _____
    _____
    _____

12. element / prism / hydrogen / sun

    _____
    _____
    _____

Applications

# 4B Electromagnetic Spectrum

*Directions*: The diagram below represents the electromagnetic waves emitted by the sun in order from the shortest to the longest wavelengths. Match the letters of the regions of the spectrum with the proper terms listed below the diagram. Place the corresponding letter in the blank.

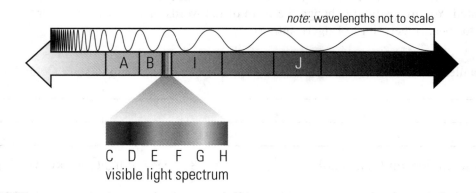

*note*: wavelengths not to scale

visible light spectrum

_____ 1. Blue light

_____ 2. Green light

_____ 3. Infrared waves

_____ 4. Orange light

_____ 5. Radio waves

_____ 6. Red light

_____ 7. Ultraviolet light

_____ 8. Violet light

_____ 9. X-rays

_____ 10. Yellow light

Applications

# 4C Structure of the Sun

*Directions*: Below is a diagram of the sun. The left half represents a model of the sun's interior. The right half represents the sun's exterior, showing both temporary and permanent features of the sun. In each blank, write the term that corresponds to the definition given; then draw a line from each term to the proper structure in the drawing.

2. _____
Pointed jets extending from the chromosphere into the corona

1. _____
The outer portion of the sun's atmosphere that extends to the heliopause.

3. _____
Severe storm on the sun that gives off x-rays and extreme ultraviolet rays

13. _____
The zone of the sun's interior where most of the thermonuclear reactions take place

4. _____
The dark inner region of a sunspot

5. _____
The brighter outer region of a sunspot

12. _____
The zone in the sun's interior where energy is transported mainly by the physical movement of plasma

6. _____
Small, dark areas on the sun's surface

11. _____
The zone in the sun's interior where energy is transported by electromagnetic waves

7. _____
The seething clumps of plasma that divide up the sun's surface

10. _____
Thin inner layer of the sun's atmosphere

8. _____
Disturbances in the corona that rise and descend in loops or jets

9. _____
Visible surface of the sun

Applications

# 4D Characteristics of the Sun

*Directions*: Listed below are 11 statements about the sun. In the spaces provided, write *True* if the statement is true and *False* if the statement is false.

_____ 1. The sun does not rotate because it is the main body around which all the other objects in our solar system revolve.

_____ 2. The number of sunspots on the sun reaches a maximum every five years.

_____ 3. The sun's axis is tilted 7° from a line perpendicular to the ecliptic.

_____ 4. Although solar flares have an effect on shortwave radio communications, sunspots do not.

_____ 5. Scientists believe that sunspots may affect the earth's weather.

_____ 6. Northern and southern lights in the sky are caused by particles from solar flares.

_____ 7. The duration of most sunspots ranges from a few days to a few weeks.

_____ 8. A large, armlike prominence is called a limb of the sun.

_____ 9. Two characteristics of solar energy are its cleanness and its low quality.

_____ 10. Solar water heaters use photovoltaic cells to collect the sun's energy.

_____ 11. Photovoltaic cells are flat, waferlike devices that convert sunlight into electricity.

## Investigation

# 4E Distance to the Sun

Each celestial body has its own "glory," or brightness. From the vantage point of the earth, the sun's glory is obviously greatest; life on this planet is vitally dependent upon our sun. Yet how much greater the God who made the sun must be—He created the heavens, earth, sun, and even light itself. Your study of the sun, a fascinating part of creation, should increase your appreciation and reverence for your infinitely powerful Lord.

## Setting Up

1. Tape or glue the piece of graph paper to one of the squares of cardboard.

2. Use intersecting diagonal lines to find the center of the second cardboard square.

3. Use a straight pin to put a pinhole in the center of the second cardboard square. Be sure that the hole is round and clear of any paper fibers.

4. Cut a slot into the center of one edge of each piece of cardboard. The slot should be the width of the thickness of the ruler, and its height should be the width of the ruler (see the diagram below).

5. Slide each piece of cardboard onto the ruler and assemble the apparatus as shown. You may need to tape the graph-paper cardboard to the ruler in order to keep it in place.

6. Clamp the ruler to the support stand with a flask clamp. Loosen the clamp wing nut so that the apparatus can be pivoted up and down.

## Goal
Determine the distance to the sun.

## Materials
calculator
straight pin
three-finger adjustable flask clamp
lab support stand
tape or glue (rubber cement is best)
1 mm ruled graph paper, 10 cm × 10 cm
two 10 cm × 10 cm pieces of cardboard
metric ruler

## Procedure and Observations
**Caution:** Never look directly at the sun.

1. Take your apparatus outside and position it so that the sun shines through the pinhole onto the graph paper. Tighten the clamp wing nut to lock the apparatus in position.

   (*Note*: It is essential that the assembly be clamped and carefully adjusted to get a correct measurement.)

2. Notice the small, round image of the sun. The spot should fall on a vertical graph line that intersects the ruler (the center of the graph paper).

3. Adjust the distance between the cardboard pieces by moving the pinhole piece until the image just fits into one square (1 mm) on the graph paper.

4. Measure the distance to the nearest tenth of a centimeter (millimeters) between the pieces of cardboard.

   a. Position of the graph-paper card:

   _____

   b. Position of the pinhole card:

   _____

   c. Record the distance |a − b|: _____ cm

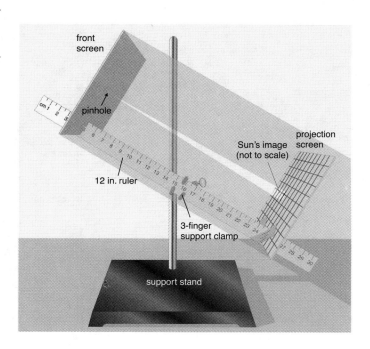

front screen

pinhole

cm 1 2 3

Sun's image (not to scale)

projection screen

12 in. ruler

3-finger support clamp

support stand

## Summing Up

1. What is the width (in centimeters) of one square on your graph paper?

   (This represents the diameter of the image.) _____

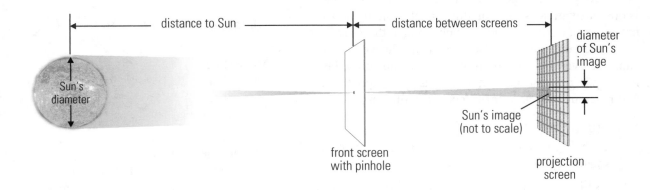

2. Using the following proportion, calculate the distance (in kilometers) to the sun.

$$\frac{\text{distance to sun (km)}}{\text{diameter of sun (1,400,000 km)}} = \frac{\text{distance between cardboard pieces}}{\text{diameter of image}}$$

   Do your calculations here.

   **Answer:** _____

3. The average distance to the sun is 150,000,000 km, which is the length of one astronomical unit (ua). If your answer is different, can you explain why?

   _____

   _____

   _____

## Investigation

# 4F Measuring Solar Heat

*Thermal energy* is the energy contained by an object due to the motion of the particles that make up the object. Thermal energy, as well as every other kind of energy, is measured in units called joules (JOOLS). Joules have the unit symbol J. *Heat* is the movement of thermal energy from one place to another. For this reason, heat is also measured in joules. Near room temperature, 4.18 J of heat must be absorbed by 1 mL (1 g) of water to raise its temperature one degree Celsius (°C). Scientists have calculated that about 1370 joules of solar energy reach each square meter at the distance of the earth's orbit in space each second. This figure is often referred to as the *solar constant*. At a location on the earth's surface, the rate of solar heating can be reduced to less than half the solar constant on an average day due to absorption and reflection of solar energy in the atmosphere. The accepted value for the solar constant at the earth's surface on an average day is 0.069 joules per square centimeter per second ($J/cm^2 \cdot s$). In this exercise, you will determine how much energy is absorbed by water under various conditions.

## Goals

Compare the effects of different materials on solar-energy collection.

Measure the solar constant.

## Materials

aluminum foil
metric ruler
flat black spray paint
plastic wrap
cardboard box
stopwatch or digital watch with seconds display
food colorings
thin glass plate
4 Styrofoam cups
50 to 250 mL graduated cylinder
4 thermometers
insulating materials (vermiculite, Styrofoam, fiberglass insulation)

## Setting Up

1. Spray the inside of the four Styrofoam cups with the flat black paint and let them dry overnight.

2. Fill the cardboard box with the material you are using for insulation. Vermiculite works best, but shredded Styrofoam, fiberglass insulation, or even crumpled newspaper will work.

3. Number the cups 1, 2, 3, and 4.

4. Nestle the four cups into the insulation so that they are well protected.

5. Place a thermometer inside each cup.

6. Cut a piece of clear plastic wrap large enough to cover the top of cup 1; cut a piece of aluminum foil for cup 2. The plate of glass will be used to cover cup 3. Cup 4 will remain uncovered.

7. Measure the diameter (*d*) of the rim of each cup. Record the diameter on the table on page SA56 in centimeters.

8. Measure the temperature of the air where you will be placing the box in the sunlight. Shield the thermometer from the sun while making this measurement.

9. At a water faucet, adjust the hot and cold water mixture until the temperature is the same as that measured in Step 8. Add the food colorings to about a liter of this water so that the color of the mixture is as black as possible.

10. Plan to do the experiment as close to noon as you can so that the rays of the sun will be as vertical as possible as they strike the water that is in the cups. However, the entire box should be shielded from the sun until after you record the initial temperature of the water in the Procedure section on the following page.

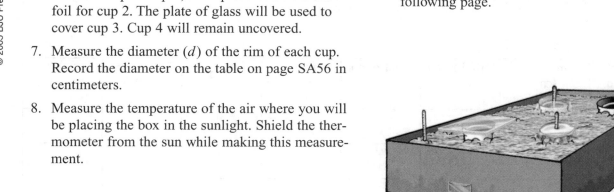

## Procedure

1.  When you are ready to start the experiment, place the box in a sunny area outside, but keep it shielded from the sun. (Use a sheet of newspaper to shadow the box, or have some classmates stand so as to block the sun.)

2.  Measure the mass of the water in the cup. The easiest way to do this is to measure the volume in milliliters, then convert the volume to mass using the relationship for water:

    $$1 \text{ mL} = 1 \text{ g}$$

    Using the graduated cylinder, fill one cup to just a few millimeters below the rim. Note in milliliters how much water was required to fill the cup. Record this value in the table as the mass of the water. (If a baking measuring cup is used, 1 oz. is equal to approximately 30 mL.)

3.  Add the same amount of water to the other three cups. Record these volumes in the table as mass for each cup.

4.  Measure the initial temperature of each cup of water and record it on the table in °C.

5.  Poke a hole in each cover material mentioned in the Setting Up section (except the glass plate). Cover each cup with its respective cover so that the thermometer protrudes from the hole.

6.  Remove the sun shield and allow the sun's rays to strike the cups. Gently stir the water in each cup with the thermometers after about 5 minutes. Note the final temperatures of each after exactly 10 minutes and record them on the table.

7.  Calculate the temperature change ($t_{final} - t_{initial}$) and record it on the table.

8.  Calculate the surface area of the water exposed to the sunlight, using the formula

    $$A = \pi \frac{d^2}{4},$$

    where $A$ is the area of the cup and $d$ is the diameter. If you do not have a pi key on your calculator, use the value $\pi = 3.14$. Record this value in the table for each cup.

9.  Calculate the joules absorbed by each cup, using the following formula:

    $$\text{energy absorbed} = E = \frac{4.18 \text{ J}}{g \cdot °C} \times \text{mass of water} \times \text{change in temperature}$$

    Record the results in the column labeled "Energy ($E$)."

10. Calculate the solar constant (for cup 4 only) using the following formula:

    $$\text{solar constant} = \frac{E}{\text{area} \times \text{elapsed time (seconds)}}$$

    (Remember that 10 min $\times$ 60 s/min = 600 s.)

| Cup # | Mass of water (g) | Diameter (d) (cm) | Initial temp. (°C) | Final temp. (°C) | Temp. change (°C) | Area (A) (cm²) | Energy (E) (J) | Solar constant (J/cm²·S) |
|---|---|---|---|---|---|---|---|---|
| 1 | | | | | | | | |
| 2 | | | | | | | | |
| 3 | | | | | | | | |
| 4 | | | | | | | | |

## Summing Up

1. How do the final temperatures of the four cups compare?

   _____

   _____

   _____

2. What do you think caused the difference?

   _____

   _____

   _____

3. Why was it necessary to paint the cup black and use darkened water?

   _____

   _____

   _____

4. Why was it necessary to insulate the cups?

   _____

   _____

   _____

5. Why does it work best to have the water nearly the same temperature as the air?

   _____

   _____

   _____

6. Examine the results for the solar constant. Would your results be closer to the accepted value in summer or winter? Why?

   _____

   _____

   _____

## Go a Step Further

1. What do you think would happen if you were to repeat the experiment, using different-colored cellophane covers for each cup?

   _____

   _____

   _____

2. Repeat the experiment, using different-colored filters. What happened?

   _____

   _____

   Why? _____

   _____

3. Which cup apparatus would be most effective when determining the solar constant on a particular day? Why?

_____

_____

_____

4. Compare your results for the solar constant with the accepted value given at the beginning of the investigation. Suggest reasons why your results may be less than that value.

_____

_____

_____

Investigation
# 4G  Observing the Sun

Looking at the sun without protection can be hazardous. The intensity of light emitted from the sun is sufficient to cause blindness to the unaided eye in just a matter of seconds. The danger is even greater with telescopic viewing, which concentrates the intensity of the light. Filters are available for telescopes, but even then you must exercise caution. Filters that are designed to fit into the eyepiece of a telescope are especially dangerous. Heat from sunlight concentrated on filters can cause them to crack, and if you are viewing when the crack occurs, the sunlight can damage your eye. Sun screens that fit over the objective lens or in front of a mirror are safer, but even then care must be taken to insure that the filter is not scratched or torn before use.

There are less hazardous ways to observe the sun, however. One technique is called the projection method. This activity will provide you with several different ways of projecting the sun's image to indirectly observe the sun. The methods in Part 1 are useful for observing the sun's disk and eclipses; in Part 2 you can use a telescope to see sunspots.

## Goal
Observe the solar disk.

## Materials
two sheets stiff card stock 8 ½ × 11 in. (or larger); one side must be white

masking tape

aluminum foil

sewing pin

(optional) large corrugated cardboard moving box

## PART 1: OBSERVING WITHOUT A TELESCOPE

### Setting Up

1. Cut a circular hole about 3 cm in diameter at the exact center of one piece of card stock.

2. Cut out a 5 cm square of aluminum foil. Tape the foil to the card stock so that there will be no light leaks.

3. Prick a small hole in the center of the foil square with a pin so that the pinhole is centered over the hole in the card.

4. (Optional) If available, a large moving box can be used as a "solar theater." The taller the box, the larger will be the sun's image. Tape shut and seal the bottom flaps. Cut a hole in a side of the box about a third of the way from the bottom in the size and shape of your face. Tape the blank card stock in the center of the bottom inside the box. Cut a 3 cm hole in a flap near the center of the top of the box. Tape the flaps down and seal any gaps. Tape the card with the pinhole constructed in Steps 2 and 3 over the hole in the flap.

### Procedure and Observations

1. Have another person support the blank card stock on the ground with the white side facing the sun. The card should be perpendicular to the sun's rays. Hold the card with the pinhole approximately 1 m from the card on the ground and parallel to it. Position it so that the lower card is shaded by the upper one. (See Figure 2.)

2. A faint image of the sun's disk should be visible within the shadow falling on the lower card stock. Adjust the distance between the two cards to maximize the brightness of the image while still preserving any details. Large sunspots may be visible on a clear day.

3. Trace the outline of the solar disk on the paper.

4. Look for any dark spots in the image of the sun.

5. (Optional) Hold the "solar theater" box so that the top is perpendicular to the sun's rays. The observer places his face into the hole cut in the side. Try to seal out all extra light. After the eyes adjust to the darkness, a fairly bright image of the sun should be visible on the screen at the bottom of the box. Look for dark spots in the disk of the sun.

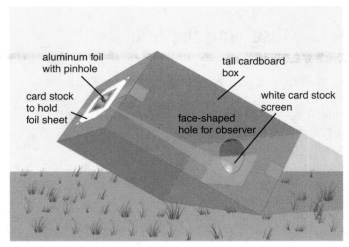

Figure 1

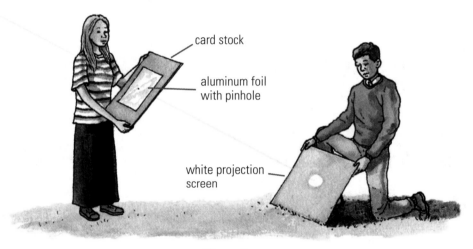

Figure 2

## PART 2: OBSERVING WITH A TELESCOPE

### Procedures

1. Prepare the telescope. Cap or otherwise cover the finder scope if one is present. (This will prevent burns or eliminate the temptation to look at the sun through the finder.) Insert the lowest-power ocular into the eyepiece holder. Cut a hole in the card stock large enough so that it can fit over the end of the telescope. This will form a shadow for the image of the sun.

2. Set up the telescope as shown in Figure 3. Aim the telescope toward the sun. Looking at the telescope's shadow on the ground, pan and tilt the telescope tube until its shadow is completely circular. Lock the mount in this position. (*Note:* As the sun's position changes with time, the telescope's aim will have to be adjusted.)

### Goal
Indirectly observe the solar disk and sunspots.

### Materials
1 sheet of stiff white card stock
refractor telescope or binoculars
sun shield
(optional) solar projection screen
(optional) large piece of mirror glass

3. **Do not look through the telescope at any time.**
Hold the card stock approximately a meter away
from the lens so that the telescope's image falls on
the card stock. It may take a little patience and time
to locate the sun in the center of the telescopic
image. (Note that the telescope eyepiece does not
have to be focused for this procedure. Move the
card stock toward and away from the eyepiece to
focus the image.)

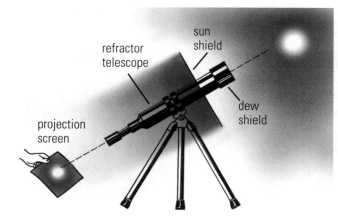

**Figure 3**

4. You may also set up the telescope to project an
image onto the wall or a projection screen in the
classroom as in Figure 4. Hold a plate-glass mirror
outside the building so as to direct the sun's rays
through an open window into the telescope. (This
works best if the mirror can be propped on a post or
clamped in position on a pole. The mirror needs to
be steady.)

**Figure 4**

5. Trace the outline of the solar disk on the card stock.

6. Look for dark spots in the image of the sun. Mark them with a pencil on
the card stock. Write the date and time on the sketch.

7. If possible, observe and sketch the sunspots again in several hours and
again in a day or two. Be sure to time and date any additional sketches.

Be sure you focus the image,
not the focal point, on the
paper. The focal point will be a
bright spot very close to the
eyepiece that can burn your
paper, whereas the image of
the sun will be quite large, not
nearly so bright, and fairly distant from the eyepiece.

## Summing Up

1. Which of the methods described should work best? In what way would the results be better with this method?

   _____

   _____

   _____

2. Were sunspots seen with the pinhole method? _____

   with the telescope method? _____

3. If sunspots were observed over several sessions, what changes were noticed?

   _____

   _____

   _____

4. If two or more observations of sunspots were sketched, determine from the sketches the direction of rotation of the sun in the image and the rotational poles of the sun.

   _____

   _____

   _____

# 5 THE PLANETS

Applications

## 5A Classification of Planets

*Directions*: Fill in the blanks below with the correct information. First, write the definitions for inferior, superior, terrestrial, and Jovian. Then, in the first column, write the planets in order; in the second column indicate which planets are inferior or superior; in the third column indicate which planets are terrestrial or Jovian.

Inferior: _____

_____

Superior: _____

_____

Terrestrial: _____

_____

Jovian: _____

_____

| Planets | Inferior/Superior | Terrestrial/Jovian |
|---|---|---|
| _____ | _____ | _____ |
| _____ | _____ | _____ |
| _____ | _____ | _____ |
| _____ | _____ | _____ |
| _____ | _____ | _____ |
| _____ | _____ | _____ |
| _____ | _____ | _____ |
| _____ | _____ | _____ |
| _____ | _____ | _____ |

Applications
# 5B Characteristics of Planets

## PART 1

*Directions*: Write the word in the puzzle that correctly completes the corresponding statement. All of the words refer to planets. Complete the definition at the end of the exercise.

1. Johannes _____ developed three laws to describe the motions of planets.

2. The characteristic shape of the orbits of planets is called an _____.

3. The astronomical term for brightness is _____.

4. The word *planet* means _____.

5. The point closest to the sun in a planet's orbit is called the _____.

6. The slower-moving superior planets appear to reverse their direction of travel when the earth catches up and passes them. This illusion is called _____ motion.

7. A planet's size and mass determine its _____ gravity.

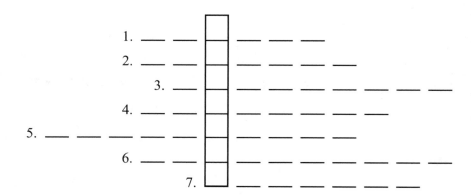

The most massive bodies orbiting the sun are _____.

# PART 2

*Directions*: Record your responses in the spaces provided.

1. If you were on Mercury, would the earth ever demonstrate retrograde motion? Why or why not?

   _____

   _____

2. Imagine that a new planet with about the same size and characteristics as Pluto were discovered only 0.614 ua from the sun. Is it likely that this planet's magnitude would be greater than Venus's? Why or why not?

   _____

   _____

3. If you weighed 740 N on the earth, what would you weigh on Pluto? _____

   What would you weigh on Jupiter? _____

   Would your mass also change? Why or why not? _____

   _____

   _____

4. If you lived on Saturn, what would be the brightest planet in the evening sky?

   _____

5. Imagine that you are looking through a telescope at a bright pinpoint of light low in the southern sky. As you watch the light, you notice that it seems to flicker intermittently. Are you looking at a star or a planet? How do you know?

   _____

   _____

   _____

   _____

6. List three factors that affect a planet's brightness.

   _____

   _____

7. From our view on the earth, Mercury and Venus appear to go through phases like the moon. This phenomenon occurs because the orbits of Mercury and Venus are inside the earth's orbit. If you lived on Uranus, what planets would you see go through phases?

   _____

   _____

8. From the data in Appendix A3, which planet would you expect to have the greatest bulge at the equator? Why?

   _____

   _____

© 2005 BJU Press. Reproduction prohibited.

Applications
## 5C Features of Planets

*Directions*: This exercise covers material from Appendix A3. For each question, darken in the letter corresponding to the correct planet. Numbers located in parentheses at the end of a question represent the total number of correct answers.

| | | | | | | | | | |
|---|---|---|---|---|---|---|---|---|---|
| M | V | E | M | J | S | U | N | P | 1. The largest planet |
| M | V | E | M | J | S | U | N | P | 2. The smallest planet |
| M | V | E | M | J | S | U | N | P | 3. The inferior planets (2) |
| M | V | E | M | J | S | U | N | P | 4. Most circular orbits (2) |
| M | V | E | M | J | S | U | N | P | 5. Have fifteen or more known moons (3) |
| M | V | E | M | J | S | U | N | P | 6. Earth's nearest neighbor |
| M | V | E | M | J | S | U | N | P | 7. Have polar ice caps (3) |
| M | V | E | M | J | S | U | N | P | 8. Discovered less than 1° from its calculated position |
| M | V | E | M | J | S | U | N | P | 9. Morning and evening stars (2) |
| M | V | E | M | J | S | U | N | P | 10. Have fewer than four known moons (5) |
| M | V | E | M | J | S | U | N | P | 11. Contains the Great Red Spot |
| M | V | E | M | J | S | U | N | P | 12. Orbit is the most eccentric and tipped at the greatest angle |
| M | V | E | M | J | S | U | N | P | 13. Have atmospheres so dense that one cannot see through them (5) |
| M | V | E | M | J | S | U | N | P | 14. Have no known moons (2) |
| M | V | E | M | J | S | U | N | P | 15. Has more than a thousand rings |
| M | V | E | M | J | S | U | N | P | 16. Fastest-rotating planet |
| M | V | E | M | J | S | U | N | P | 17. Discovered by William Herschel |
| M | V | E | M | J | S | U | N | P | 18. Contains Cassini's Division |
| M | V | E | M | J | S | U | N | P | 19. Reddish in color |
| M | V | E | M | J | S | U | N | P | 20. Have one known moon (2) |
| M | V | E | M | J | S | U | N | P | 21. Its largest moon (Titan) has an atmosphere |
| M | V | E | M | J | S | U | N | P | 22. Planet is tipped on its side compared to the ecliptic |
| M | V | E | M | J | S | U | N | P | 23. Planets that occasionally switch places in planet order (2) |
| M | V | E | M | J | S | U | N | P | 24. Has two known moons |
| M | V | E | M | J | S | U | N | P | 25. Has a single thin ring |
| M | V | E | M | J | S | U | N | P | 26. Has the smallest orbit |
| M | V | E | M | J | S | U | N | P | 27. Has eleven faint rings |
| M | V | E | M | J | S | U | N | P | 28. Has the Galilean moons |
| M | V | E | M | J | S | U | N | P | 29. Planets that undergo transits as viewed from Earth (2) |
| M | V | E | M | J | S | U | N | P | 30. Has both water and oxygen in abundance |
| M | V | E | M | J | S | U | N | P | 31. The superior planets (6) |
| M | V | E | M | J | S | U | N | P | 32. Has the greatest visual magnitude |
| M | V | E | M | J | S | U | N | P | 33. Has a moon that revolves in the direction opposite all its other moons |
| M | V | E | M | J | S | U | N | P | 34. Closest planet to the sun |
| M | V | E | M | J | S | U | N | P | 35. Exhibits reverse rotation compared to other planets (disregard rotational-axis inclination) (3) |

# 5D Retrograde Motion

Retrograde motion was very puzzling to early astronomers who studied the planets. Night after night, as they plotted the position of any one of the superior planets in the sky, the planet would steadily move forward and then, for several nights, would appear to move backward. Then it would resume a forward path. Did the planet actually move backward? This investigation will help you understand the apparent motion of the planets.

## Procedure

Note that the two planets in the diagram on the next page are revolving "counterclockwise," as all planets do. The inner circle shows the orbit of the earth. The outer circle shows the orbit of Mars. The similarly lettered positions in each planet's orbit represent their positions at the same time. The successively lettered positions are one month apart in the orbits.

1. Using your ruler, draw a line to connect the centers of the two marks labeled *A* in the diagram on the following page (connect the earth's orbit with Mars's orbit). Then connect the other marks in the same way. When you are finished, all the *A*s should be connected, all the *B*s, all the *C*s, and so on.

2. Using your protractor, measure the angle formed between each line you drew and the reference direction (to a star) indicated by the line passing through the earth. Record these angles in the table provided. On the second diagram, you will plot the positions of Mars as seen from the earth using the table.

3. Place your protractor on the reference line above the observer's head in the diagram on page SA69. Place a mark on the diagram along the edge of your protractor at the same angle that you recorded for month *A*.

4. Using your ruler, measure 10 cm from the center of the observer's reference line through the mark you made for *A*. Place a dot at the 10 cm mark and label it *A*.

5. Repeat Steps 3 and 4 for *B* through *I*, making each successive line 0.1 cm (1 mm) shorter. This will help to keep the time progression of the dots clear to you.

6. Draw an arrow from dot *A* to dot *B*, another from *B* to *C*, and so forth.

## Goal
Demonstrate how the illusion of retrograde motion occurs.

## Materials
pencil
protractor
ruler

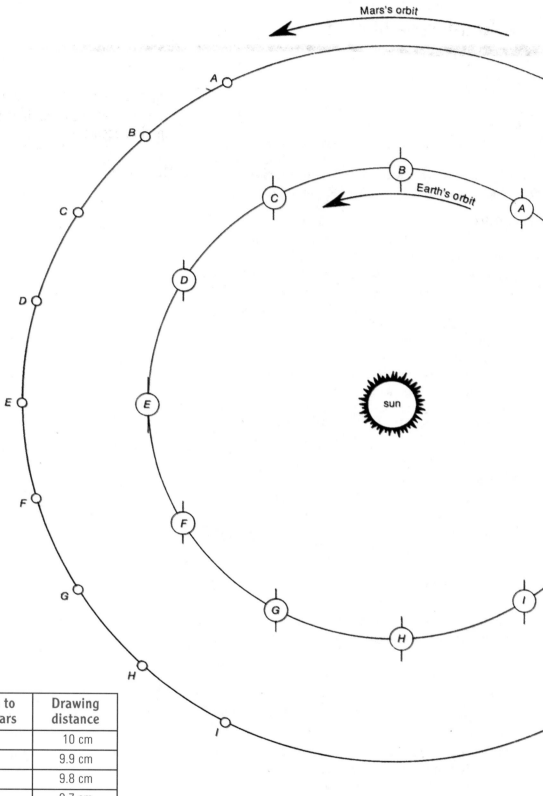

| Month | Angle to see Mars | Drawing distance |
|---|---|---|
| A | | 10 cm |
| B | | 9.9 cm |
| C | | 9.8 cm |
| D | | 9.7 cm |
| E | | 9.6 cm |
| F | | 9.5 cm |
| G | | 9.4 cm |
| H | | 9.3 cm |
| I | | 9.2 cm |

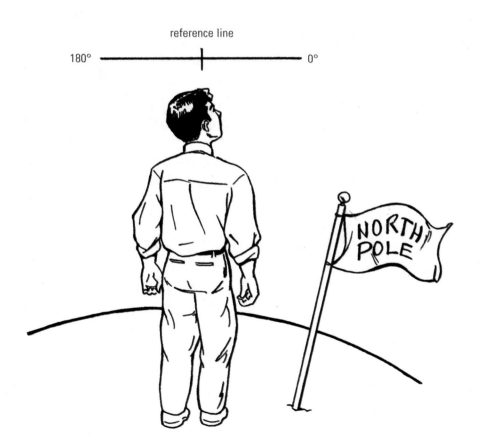

reference line

180° ————————————|———————————— 0°

## Summing Up

1. Look at the first diagram showing both the earth's and Mars's orbits. Did Mars ever move backwards?

   _____

2. Look at the second diagram showing the orbit of Mars as seen from the earth. Between which lettered months did Mars appear to move backwards?

   _____

3. By looking at your diagrams, explain whether Mars is really moving backwards or whether it just appears to be moving backwards.

   _____

   _____

   _____

4. The earth orbits the sun in 365 days; Mars orbits the sun in 687 Earth days. Would the difference in orbital time have anything to do with this illusion of moving backwards?

   _____

5. Why do you think the superior planets are the only planets that exhibit retrograde motion?

   _____

   _____

   _____

6. If you were on Venus, would the earth appear to show retrograde motion? Why?

   _____

   _____

   _____

7. When our observer measured the angles of sight to Mars, he made the measurements at the same time each day. Did he use solar days or sidereal days? Why? (*Hint*: Carefully study the first diagram and Investigation 2H.)

   _____

   _____

   _____

Investigation

# 5E Kepler's First Law

Kepler's first law of planetary motion states that planets move in ellipses with the sun at one focus. An ellipse is the shape formed by the shadow of a circular disk held at an angle to the light or when a cone is cut at an angle.

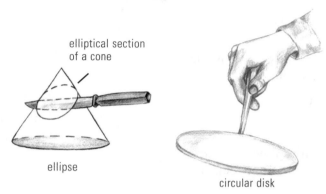

elliptical section
of a cone

ellipse

circular disk

In math, an ellipse is defined as the path of a point moving around two fixed points called *foci* (singular, *focus*). If the distances from the moving point to the two foci are added together, the sum is a constant, regardless of the location of the moving point.

This mathematical definition of an ellipse relates the ellipse to Tycho Brahe's observations that Kepler studied and allows us to draw it with simple equipment.

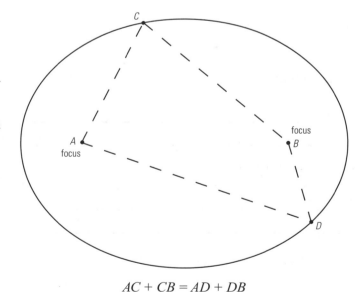

$$AC + CB = AD + DB$$

## Goal
Draw an ellipse.

## Materials
heavy cardboard, one piece 8 ½ in. × 11 in.
   (or larger)
white paper, three sheets 8 ½ in. × 11 in.
string, 25 cm
ruler
pencil (a mechanical pencil works best)
masking tape
two thumbtacks or push pins

## Procedure

1. On a sheet of white paper, draw a pair of perpendicular lines to represent axes. Place their point of intersection near the center of the paper. Draw the axis that is parallel to the long edge of the paper longer than the other axis.

2. Using a ruler, plot two points 4 cm apart on the longer axis, centering the points on either side of the intersection (one point 2 cm to the right and the other 2 cm to the left). These points are going to be the foci of the ellipse.

3. Lay your paper on the piece of cardboard and tape it in place.

4. Place a thumbtack firmly into the paper (and cardboard) at each focus.

5. Tie the string in a 20 cm loop. You may need two people to get the loop the right length and tied tightly.

6. Place the loop over the tacks, keeping the knot at the top of the paper and to one end.

7. Place a pencil inside the string at the knot.

8. Pull the string taut with the pencil point. Hold the pencil vertically with the string less than 0.5 cm from the pencil point. Place the pencil point on the paper and begin tracing out the ellipse, keeping the string taut as you go.

9. When you encounter the knot, tip the pencil slightly toward the center of the ellipse and slip the knot around the pencil point. Keep the point in contact with the paper.

10. Return the pencil to a vertical position and continue around the ellipse until the figure is closed. It is important that the string remain taut at all times.

11. Repeat steps 1 through 10 for foci that are 6 cm and 8 cm apart.

## Observations

1. Look carefully at your three ellipses. What relationship can you see between the distance between the foci, the average distance the pencil is from the foci, and the shape of the ellipse?

   _____

   _____

2. Mark two points on two different places on your first ellipse and label them *A* and *B*. Measure the distance from to *A* to the first focus and from *A* to the second focus. Add these two measurements. Now measure the distances from the foci to *B* and add the distances.

   Are your two answers close? _____

   Does this follow the mathematical definition of an ellipse?

   _____

|  | Point *A* | Point *B* |
|---|---|---|
| Distance to focus 1 |  |  |
| Distance to focus 2 |  |  |
| Total distance |  |  |

## Summing Up

1. According to Chapter 5, which one of the three ellipses best approximates the earth's orbit? How do you know?

   _____

   _____

2. According to Chapter 2, how did Kepler conclude that the paths of planets are ellipses, not circles as Copernicus had said?

   _____

   _____

## Investigation

# 5F Kepler's Second Law

Kepler's second law of planetary motion states that an imaginary line from the center of the sun to the center of a planet always sweeps over an equal area in an equal amount of time. This means that a planet moves faster at the perihelion and slower at the aphelion.

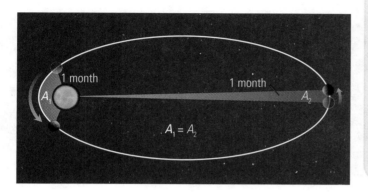

## Goal

Demonstrate that a planet moves faster at the perihelion and slower at the aphelion because it sweeps through an equal area in equal time.

## Materials

rocks, pieces of chalk, weighted paper cups, etc. (for markers), (21)

rope, 24 m or longer

stopwatch or digital watch with seconds display

tape measure (metric)

chalkboard protractor

## Setting Up

1. On a large flat area, stretch out the rope in a straight line. Anchor both ends with large rocks, if required. This is the base line from which all the other measurements will be made.

2. Measure 10 m 36 cm along the base line from the right end and place a rock at that spot. This rock will represent the sun.

3. Place a protractor and the 0 m end of the tape measure at the "sun"; then move the free end of the tape measure clockwise from the base line according to the increments on the table below. Place a rock at the indicated distance at each move. This will complete half of the ellipse.

4. Start at the sun and repeat Step 3 in a counter-clockwise direction to complete the other half of the ellipse.

5. Remove the base line and the two rock anchors.

| Distance from sun mark | Angle from first mark |
|---|---|
| 10 m 40 cm (10.40 m) | 20° |
| 10 m 71 cm (10.71 m) | 56° |
| 11 m 26 cm (11.26 m) | 85° |
| 11 m 84 cm (11.84 m) | 108° |
| 12 m 42 cm (12.42 m) | 128° |
| 12 m 85 cm (12.85 m) | 145° |
| 13 m 14 cm (13.14 m) | 160° |
| 13 m 29 cm (13.29 m) | 174° |

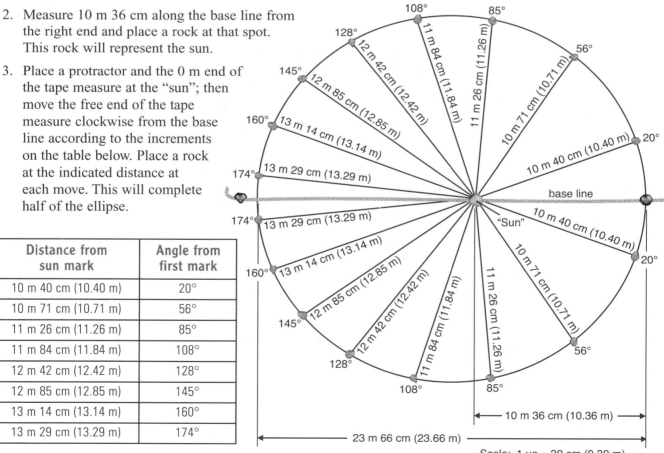

## Procedure and Observations

1. Stand at any of the markers. (Two or three people can do this at once, but they should start at different markers.)

2. Using a stopwatch, have another student call out "move" every two seconds. The "planets" should move around the ellipse at least twice. You should move from marker to marker in a counterclockwise fashion every two seconds.

3. Did you ever have to speed up to keep in time? If so, at what part in the ellipse?

_____

## Summing Up

1. According to Kepler's second law, if you were to calculate the area of each triangle on the ellipse, represented by two adjacent markers and the "sun," what would you discover? Remember that $A = \frac{1}{2}bh$.

_____

2. Why did your speed change at some places on the orbit?

_____

_____

_____

_____

Investigation

# 5G Kepler's Third Law

You have learned that all of the planets in the solar system have different orbital shapes. For example, Venus and Neptune have nearly circular orbits, whereas Pluto has an eccentric orbit. Kepler's third law of planetary motion states that cubes of their average distances in ua from the sun ($D^3$) is proportional to the squares of the periods of the planets in years ($P^2$). In an equation, this idea can be expressed as

$$D^3 = KP^2,$$

where $K$ is a constant called Kepler's constant. This constant applies to everything orbiting around the same center of gravity. For example, in the solar system, the same Kepler's constant is used for all planets, asteroids, and comets to relate their average distances to the sun and their orbital periods. Jupiter's 63+ moons use a different constant because Jupiter is the center of that gravitational system.

If orbital distances are given in astronomical units and periods in Earth years, Kepler's constant is

$$K = 1 \ \frac{\text{ua}^3}{\text{y}^2}.$$

## Goals

Demonstrate that Kepler's third law works regardless of the shape of a planet's orbit.

Use data to predict the average distance from a planet to the sun.

Use data to predict the orbital period of a planet in Earth years.

## Materials

scientific calculator

## Procedure and Observations

1. Fill in the following table. In the term $D^3$, the exponent shows that the base ($D$) is used as a factor three times ($D \times D \times D$). In $P^2$, the base ($P$) is used as a factor twice ($P \times P$).

| Planet name | P (Period of orbit in years) | D (Average distance from Sun in ua) | P² | D³ |
|---|---|---|---|---|
| Mercury | 0.2408 | 0.3871 | | |
| Venus | 0.6152 | 0.7233 | | |
| Earth | 1.000 | 1.000 | | |
| Mars | 1.881 | 1.524 | | |
| Jupiter | 11.87 | 5.203 | | |
| Saturn | 29.46 | 9.539 | | |
| Uranus | 84.07 | 19.19 | | |
| Neptune | 164.8 | 30.06 | | |
| Pluto | 248.5 | 39.53 | | |

2. Did the squares of the periods equal the cubes of the distance in your table? _____

3. Given the period, fill in the following distances in the table. For example, given that the orbital period of the fictional planet Gargolith is 8.000 y, calculate the average distance of the planet from the sun. Substitute 8.000 y for $P$ in the formula. Note that Kepler's constant provides the units for the answer.

$$D^3 = KP^2$$

$$D^3 = (8.000 \text{ y})^2 \frac{\text{ua}^3}{\text{y}^2}$$

$$D^3 = (64.00 \cancel{\text{y}^2}) \frac{\text{ua}^3}{\cancel{\text{y}^2}} = 64.00 \text{ ua}^3$$

$$\sqrt[3]{D^3} = \sqrt[3]{64.00 \text{ ua}^3}$$

$$D = 4.000 \text{ ua}$$

| Planet name | Orbital period, $P$ (years) | Average distance, $D$ (ua) |
|---|---|---|
| Gargolith | 8.000 | 4.000 |
| Aleph | 5.196 | |
| Beth | 4.000 | |
| Gimel | 3.000 | |
| Daleth | 2.828 | |
| Earleth | 1.000 | |

4. Did the average distance from the sun increase or decrease as the period length shortened?

_____

5. Fill in the orbital periods in the following table, given the average distance from the sun. For example, given that the average distance from the sun of the planet Gargolith is 4.000 ua, calculate the planet's orbital period in years. Substitute 4.000 ua for $D$ in the formula. You will first have to divide both sides of the equation by Kepler's constant. How do you divide by a fraction?

$$D^3 = KP^2 = P^2 \frac{\text{ua}^3}{\text{y}^2}$$

$$D^3 \frac{\text{y}^2}{\text{ua}^3} = P^2 \left(\frac{\cancel{\text{ua}^3}}{\cancel{\text{y}^2}}\right)\left(\frac{\cancel{\text{y}^2}}{\cancel{\text{ua}^3}}\right) \quad \text{(multiply both sides by the inverted fraction)}$$

$$D^3 \frac{\text{y}^2}{\text{ua}^3} = P^2 \quad \text{or} \quad P^2 = D^3 \frac{\text{y}^2}{\text{ua}^3}$$

$$P^2 = (4.000 \text{ ua})^3 \frac{\text{y}^2}{\text{ua}^3}$$

$$P^2 = (64.00 \cancel{\text{ua}^3}) \frac{\text{y}^2}{\cancel{\text{ua}^3}} = 64.00 \text{ y}^2$$

$$\sqrt{P^2} = \sqrt{64.00 \text{ y}^2}$$

$$P = 8.000 \text{ y}$$

| Planet name | Orbital period, $P$ (years) | Average distance $D$ (ua) |
|---|---|---|
| Gargolith | 8.000 | 4.000 |
| Morris | | 0.241 |
| Volus | | 0.615 |
| Excel | | 1.000 |
| Marcus | | 1.880 |
| Jovan | | 11.862 |

6. Did the orbital period lengthen or shorten as the average distance from the sun increased?

_____

## Summing Up

1. Did Kepler's third law hold true regardless of the shape or size of the orbit? _____

2. Can you logically conclude from this investigation that the farther a planet is from the sun, the longer it takes the planet to complete one orbit? _____

3. If Kepler's constant for the solar system had been defined in terms of Jupiter years (duration of one Jupiter orbit) and Jupiter's average distance from the sun, would that affect the relationship of period to distance in Kepler's law? What would change, if anything?

_____

Investigation

# 5H Planetary Sizes

## Procedure and Observations

1. Cut out the rectangular grid and grid ruler on page SA79. Tape the grid to the sheet of cardboard.

2. In this investigation, the side of one square on the grid equals 1000 km. Calculate the diameter of each planet (in number of grid squares) and fill in the following table.

3. Since the radius is one-half of the diameter, divide the diameter (in number of grid squares) by 2 to obtain the radius (in number of grid squares). Round to one decimal place.

| Planet name | Diameter (km) | Diameter (grid squares) | Radius (grid squares) |
|---|---|---|---|
| Pluto | 2300 | | |
| Mercury | 4900 | | |
| Mars | 6800 | | |
| Venus | 12,100 | | |
| Earth | 12,800 | | |
| Neptune | 49,500 | | |
| Uranus | 51,100 | | |
| Saturn | 120,500 | | |
| Jupiter | 143,000 | | |

4. Count along the ruler the number of boxes that represent the radius of each of the nine planets.

5. Make a pencil mark in the center column of the ruler at each of these points.

6. Push the thumbtack through the "+" marks to fasten the grid ruler to the grid.

7. Push the point of a pencil through the grid at the points that you marked, and gently sweep the pencil in an arc from side to side. This will produce arcs that represent the sizes of the planets according to the scale. (See the figure below.)

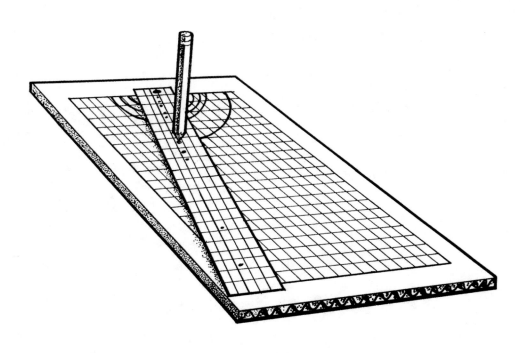

## Summing Up

1. In this investigation, you started your drawing at the edge of the paper. If you started your drawing with the ruler at the center of the paper instead, some of the planets would not fit. Which planets would not have fit?

   _____

2. Group the planets under the headings "Small," "Medium," and "Large" in the following table.

| Small | Medium | Large |
|-------|--------|-------|
|       |        |       |
|       |        |       |
|       |        |       |
|       |        |       |

3. Which two planets are the closest in size? _____

## Investigation

# 5I Planetary Distance

## Procedure and Observations

1. Calculate the distance of the planets from the sun
   in astronomical units (ua) and fill in the following
   table (1 ua = 150,000,000 km).

2. One square on the following grid represents
   150,000,000 km (1 ua). Calculate the average distance of each planet from the sun (in number of
   grid squares), and finish the table.

**Goal**
Comprehend the distance between planets
and between each planet and the sun.

**Materials**
calculator

| Planet name | Average distance (km) | Average distance (ua) | Average distance (grid squares) |
|---|---|---|---|
| Mercury | 58,500,000 | | |
| Venus | 108,000,000 | | |
| Earth | 150,000,000 | | |
| Mars | 228,000,000 | | |
| Jupiter | 780,000,000 | | |
| Saturn | 1,430,000,000 | | |
| Uranus | 2,880,000,000 | | |
| Neptune | 4,510,000,000 | | |
| Pluto | 5,930,000,000 | | |

Round the distance in grid
squares to the nearest tenth.

3. Place a small dot for each planet on the center line grid below at the appropriate
   number of grid squares from the sun.

4. Label all nine planets.

5. After the name of each planet, record its average distance from the sun in ua.

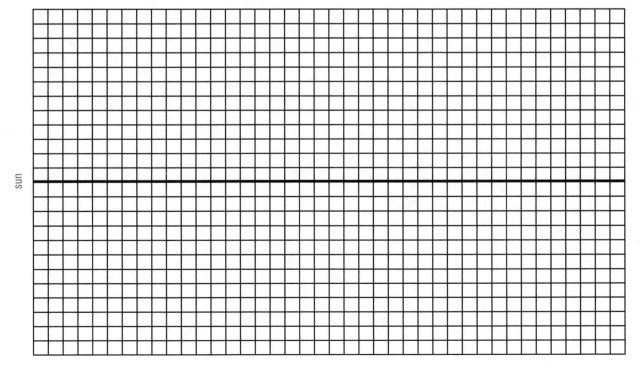

sun

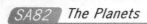 

## Summing Up

1. Which planet's average distance from the sun is 1 ua? How could this be?

   _____

   _____

2. Which planet is about five times as far from the sun as the earth is? _____

3. Name three planets, the second of which is about twice as far from the sun as the first, and the third of which is about twice as far as the second.

   _____

4. Which planet is closest to the earth? _____

5. Which planet is about three times as far from the sun as Saturn is? _____

6. The nearest star is about 39,900,000,000,000 km away. How many squares would be needed to plot it?

   _____

   One of the above squares is about 0.393 cm long. How far away (in centimeters) would the star be placed on a grid sheet if you had one large enough?

   _____

   How many meters? _____

# 6 ASTEROIDS, COMETS, AND METEORS

© 2005 BJU Press. Reproduction prohibited.

## Applications

## 6A Minor Planets

*Directions*: Match the statements on the left with the terms on the right. Place the letter of the answer on the blank of the appropriate statement. Enter the number of the statement in the corresponding lettered box on the magic square. If you complete the magic square correctly, you will find that each row, each column, and each diagonal of the square will total the same number. Write the number in the blank at the bottom. To get you started, the answer to Number 6 has been supplied.

_____ 1. Discovered the first minor planet in 1801

_____ 2. The largest minor planet

_____ 3. The brightest minor planet

_____ 4. Discovered by Heinrich Olbers one year after the first minor planet was discovered

_____ 5. Discovered by Karl Hencke in 1845

__n___ 6. A technique developed in 1890 for finding minor planets

_____ 7. Another term for *minor planet*

_____ 8. Minor planets that have similar orbits and move in groups

_____ 9. Asteroids with nearly the same orbit as Jupiter

_____ 10. A family of asteroids that comes closer to the earth than any major planet

_____ 11. An asteroid provisional number

_____ 12. First asteroid photographed showing a small satellite

_____ 13. The asteroid on which a space probe landed in 2001

_____ 14. Has one of the smallest perihelions known

_____ 15. The seventh minor planet to be discovered

_____ 16. A Trojan asteroid

a. Giuseppi Piazzi
b. 243 Ida
c. Asteroid
d. 1566 Icarus
e. Family
f. 433 Eros
g. 1 Ceres
h. 2008 BG
i. Atens
j. 4 Vesta
k. 588 Achilles
l. 5 Astraea
m. 7 Iris
n. Time-lapse photography
o. Trojan
p. 2 Pallas

| a | b | c | d |
|---|---|---|---|
| e | f | g | h |
| i | j | k | l |
| m | n **6** | o | p |

The magic number is _____.

Applications

# 6B Structure of a Comet

*Directions*: Label the parts of the comet by supplying the missing terms and information and then drawing a line from each term to the proper structure in the drawing.

**Main parts of a comet**

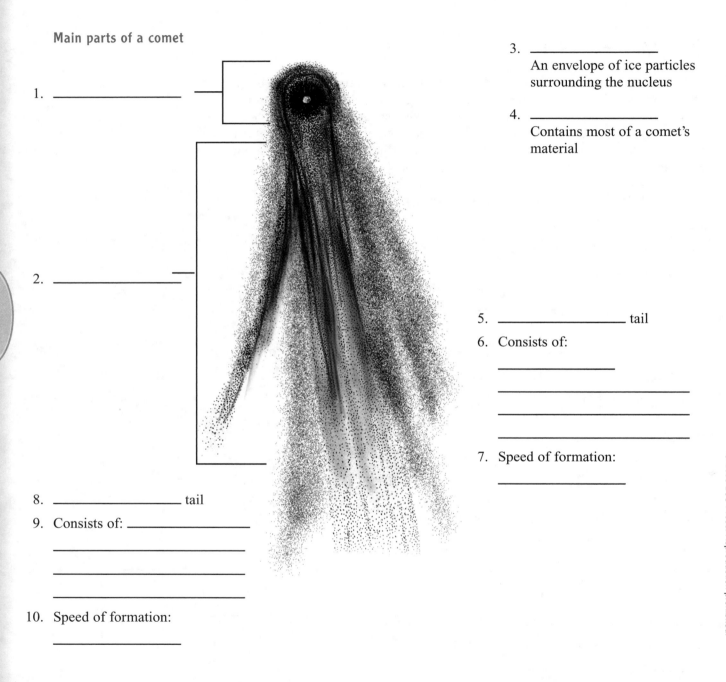

1. _____

2. _____

3. _____
   An envelope of ice particles surrounding the nucleus

4. _____
   Contains most of a comet's material

5. _____ tail

6. Consists of:

   _____

   _____

   _____

   _____

7. Speed of formation:

   _____

8. _____ tail

9. Consists of: _____

   _____

   _____

   _____

10. Speed of formation:

    _____

Applications
# 6C Famous Comets

*Directions*: Refer to Table 6-2 (page 136) and fill in the missing information in the table below.

| Comet name | Some interesting facts |
|---|---|
| Arend-Roland | had a(n) (1) _____ |
| (2) | broke into meteoroids |
| (3) | shortest known period, (4) _____ years |
| (5) | had six tails |
| Great Comet of 1843 | (6) |
| Ikeya-Seki | (7) |
| (8) | closest approach of a comet's head to Earth |
| (9) | nearly circular orbit |
| (10) | head broke into four parts |
| Shoemaker-Levy 9 | (11) |

Applications
# 6D Meteors

*Directions*: In the spaces provided, tell the difference between or among each of the terms given in complete sentences.

1. meteoroid / meteor / meteorite _____
_____
_____
_____

2. Perseids / Leonids _____
_____
_____
_____

3. sporadic meteors / shower meteors _____
_____
_____
_____

4. stones / irons / stony-irons _____
_____
_____
_____

Applications

# 6E Review: Minor Planets, Comets, Meteors

*Directions*: Read the following descriptions and decide which of the three lesser members of the solar system is being described. In the space by each statement, place an *A* if the statement describes an asteroid, a *C* if it describes a comet, or an *M* if it describes a meteor.

_____ 1. Located mostly between the orbits of Mars and Jupiter

_____ 2. May leave a lighted trail called a train

_____ 3. Called "shooting stars"

_____ 4. Has a head

_____ 5. The largest is named 1 Ceres.

_____ 6. The best-known example is named 1P/Halley.

_____ 7. May have an extremely elliptical or near-parabolic orbit

_____ 8. Hits the earth's surface most often and may form a crater

_____ 9. According to a popular theory, formed from the disintegration of a planet between Mars and Jupiter

_____ 10. Properly called minor planets

_____ 11. August 12 and November 17 are usually good viewing times.

_____ 12. Fireball

_____ 13. May have more than one tail

_____ 14. The gravitational pull of the sun or a planet can pull it apart.

_____ 15. The brightest is named 4 Vesta.

_____ 16. The rarest types are called stony-irons.

_____ 17. Many of these should be in the earth's fossil layers according to evolutionists, but very few are actually found.

## Investigation

# 6F Halley's Comet

Comet Halley is undoubtedly the most famous of all comets, both past and present. It is named after Edmund Halley (1646–1742), a contemporary of Sir Isaac Newton. Halley did not discover the comet; it had been seen many times before his lifetime. What he did do was tie together several historical sightings and show that they were all of one comet having a period of seventy-five to seventy-six years. In this investigation, you will verify his calculations and gain a greater understanding of the comet's motions.

## Procedure

1. Plot the orbit of Halley's comet. Draw a line down the center of a sheet of ¼ in. ruled graph paper to represent the major axis of the orbit. Place a large dot on the line about 1 in. (four squares or units) from the bottom of the paper to represent the sun.

2. Using the scale ¼ in. = 1 ua, place a dot at 0.6 ua below the sun to represent the comet's perihelion and another dot at 35.3 ua above the sun for the aphelion. This will form an ellipse with a *major axis* approximately 36 units long.

3. The orbit of Halley's comet is about four times as long as it is wide. Therefore, it will be 9 units across at its widest point, which is halfway between the perihelion and aphelion. Draw a line perpendicular to the major axis at a point 18 units from either end. Where the two lines cross is the ellipse's *center*.

4. On this new line, mark two points 4½ ua on each side of the major axis. The distance between these points is the orbit's *minor axis*.

5. Sketch in the orbit. This elongated elliptical orbit will pass through the four points you have drawn— the perihelion, the aphelion, and the two points at the ends of the minor axis.

6. Draw in part of the orbits of the following planets to show where the comet's orbit crosses each planet's orbit. Use these figures for radii: Earth, 1.0 ua; Mars, 1.5 ua; Jupiter, 5.2 ua; Saturn, 9.5 ua; Uranus, 19.2 ua; Neptune, 30 ua; and Pluto, 39.5 ua. Label each orbit.

## Goals

Make a map of the orbit of Halley's comet, showing its relationship to the orbits of the planets.

Calculate the period of the comet based on the dates of its last nine returns.

## Materials

calculator

ruler

graph paper, 8½ × 11 in., ¼ in. ruled

7. Place the dates of arrival at various points in the orbit, remembering that Halley's comet moves *clockwise* in its orbit, the direction opposite from the revolution of the planets.

| | |
|---|---|
| Aphelion: 1948 | Cross Jupiter's orbit: 1987 |
| Cross Neptune's orbit: 1965 | Cross Saturn's orbit: 1989 |
| Cross Uranus's orbit: 1977 | Cross Uranus's orbit: 1994 |
| Cross Saturn's orbit: 1983 | Cross Neptune's orbit: 2008 |
| Cross Jupiter's orbit: 1985 | Aphelion: 2024 |
| Perihelion: 1986 | |

This timetable shows how much the comet speeds up as it approaches the sun.

(*Note*: Although you have drawn everything in the same plane, the major axis of comet Halley's orbit is actually angled 17° below the ecliptic plane. There is, therefore, no danger of its colliding with any of the planets, even though it might appear on the drawing that there is.)

8. Calculate the period of Halley's comet. The numbers in the table (to the right) are the dates of the comet's last nine returns (perihelion passages).

   a. Subtract each pair of numbers and record the differences in the table.

   b. Add the nine numbers and record the total in the table.

   c. Compute the average of the nine numbers, rounding it to the nearest tenth of a year. This is a reasonably accurate figure for the period of Halley's comet.

| Years | Differences |
|-------|-------------|
| 1301–1378 | |
| 1378–1456 | |
| 1456–1531 | |
| 1531–1607 | |
| 1607–1682 | |
| 1682–1759 | |
| 1759–1835 | |
| 1835–1910 | |
| 1910–1986 | |
| Total | |
| Average | |

## Observations

1. Imagine that the line drawn down the center of the orbital plot is a mirror. Is the right side of the orbit a reflection (mirror image) of the left side? Is the front half of the orbit (the half toward the sun) a reflection of the back half (the half away from the sun)?

   _____

   _____

2. Refer to the dates of arrival you have placed on your graph. About how much time does Halley's comet spend in the front half of its orbit? (Halley's comet spends about four times as much time in the back half of its orbit as it does in the front half.)

   _____

3. Based on your observations and the information given in Question 2, why do you think Halley's comet cannot be seen most of the time?

   _____

   _____

4. Does Halley's comet return after exactly the same number of years from one passage to the next? Explain your answer.

   _____

   _____

5. For the twenty-seven times that Halley's comet has been observed since 239 BC, its period has varied from seventy-four to seventy-nine years. According to your data for the last nine returns, did its period vary that much?

   _____

## Summing Up

1. Based on your calculation for the period of Halley's comet, in what year should Halley's comet make its next return to its perihelion?

   _____

2. At what point in its orbit does Halley's comet move the most rapidly? At what point does it move the most slowly?

   _____

3. Why is there so little danger that Halley's comet will ever collide with one of the planets, even though in an overhead view of the solar system, its orbit appears to cross the orbits of the planets?

   _____

4. Name two differences between the earth's orbit and the orbit of Halley's comet.

_____

_____

_____

_____

5. If the orbit of Halley's comet is 35.9 ua long, what is its length in kilometers (miles)? If its perihelion distance is 0.6 ua, what is the distance in kilometers (miles) of its approach to the sun?

_____

6. Where is Halley's comet in its orbit this year? _____

_____

# 6G Finding the Radiant of the Leonids

As the earth moves through the orbiting debris of a comet, innumerable meteoroids are swept up and produce a meteor shower. The visual effect is similar to driving through a heavy snow squall at night. In the reflected light from the headlights, the snowflakes seem to be coming at the car from a point ahead of the vehicle. In the same way, the shower meteors appear to radiate from a point in the sky. This point is called the meteor shower *radiant*. For the Leonid shower, which arrives about November 17 each year, the radiant is in the constellation Leo. In this investigation, you will plot the positions of the main stars of the constellation Leo, the paths of a number of meteors observed during the Leonid shower, and the location of the Leonid radiant.

## Goal
Plot the radiant of the Leonid meteors.

## Materials
ruler
two colored pencils

## Procedure

1. Using a colored pencil, plot the locations of the nine most prominent stars of the constellation Leo on the grid provided on page SA93. The coordinates are given below.

| Prominent stars of Leo | Coordinates | |
|:---:|:---:|:---:|
| | Right ascension | Declination |
| 1 | 10$^h$06$^m$ | +12° |
| 2 | 11$^h$47$^m$ | +15° |
| 3 | 10$^h$18$^m$ | +20° |
| 4 | 11$^h$12$^m$ | +21° |
| 5 | 09$^h$43$^m$ | +24° |
| 6 | 10$^h$15$^m$ | +23° |
| 7 | 10$^h$05$^m$ | +17° |
| 8 | 11$^h$12$^m$ | +16° |
| 9 | 09$^h$51$^m$ | +26° |

2. Using a second colored pencil, plot the locations of the starting point and the stopping point of the first meteor from the table below.

3. Connect the starting and stopping points of the first meteor with a line.

4. Draw an arrowhead at the stopping point to show the direction that the meteor was traveling.

5. Repeat Steps 2 through 4 for meteors 2 through 15.

| Meteors | Start Right ascension | Declination | Stop Right ascension | Declination |
|---|---|---|---|---|
| 1 | 09h00m | +16.0° | 08h10m | +12.0° |
| 2 | 12h25m | +5.0° | 13h10m | −1.0° |
| 3 | 09h20m | +32.0° | 08h45m | 39 5° |
| 4 | 10h35m | +40.0° | 10h45m | +48.0° |
| 5 | 12h00m | +32.0° | 13h00m | +37.0° |
| 6 | 11h50m | +34.0° | 12h40m | +40.0° |
| 7 | 10h55m | +5.0° | 11h13m | −2.0° |
| 8 | 09h44m | +12.0° | 09h15m | +0.0° |
| 9 | 10h47m | +3.0° | 11h05m | −6.0° |
| 10 | 12h10m | +7.0° | 13h05m | +4.0° |
| 11 | 08h58m | +30.0° | 07h40m | +39.5° |
| 12 | 12h10m | +26.0° | 12h44m | +27.0° |
| 13 | 09h20m | +16.0° | 08h03m | +6.7° |
| 14 | 11h40m | +32.0° | 12h12m | +35.5° |
| 15 | 08h35m | +36.0° | 08h00m | +41.0° |

6.  Using a ruler, extend the meteor paths backwards to find the point from which they all appear to be coming. Mark this point with an asterisk (*). This is the radiant of the Leonid meteors.

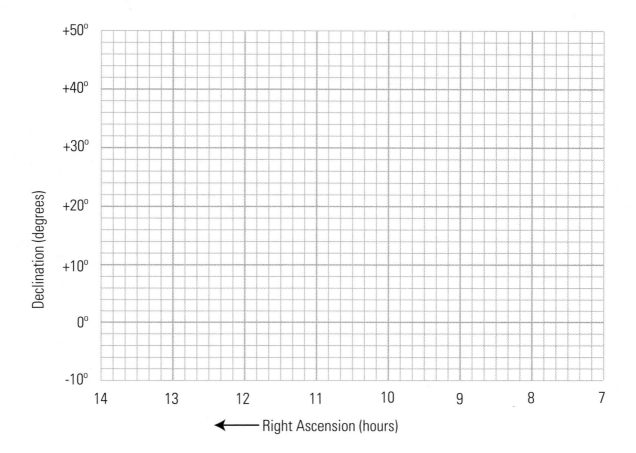

## Summing Up

1.  You should have noticed that when you plotted meteor 10 and extended its path backwards, it did not come from the same direction in Leo as the other meteors did. This happened because it is a sporadic meteor. According to your text, what is the definition of *sporadic meteor*?

    _____

    _____

2.  According to your text, why are the meteors that you studied in this activity called the Leonid meteors?

    _____

3.  Are the Leonid meteors shower or sporadic meteors? _____

4.  Give the celestial coordinates (RA, DEC) of the shower radiant. _____

# 7 THE MOON

Applications
## 7A Conditions on the Moon

### PART 1:

*Directions*: List four of the problems or disadvantages people would have to face if they tried to live on the equator of the moon. Can you think of any others? List them on the extra lines

1. _____
2. _____
3. _____
4. _____
* _____
* _____

### PART 2:

*Directions*: Write clues that relate to the moon for each of the crossword answers below.

```
A S T R O N A U T S
  E               P
V R           L   H
A T M O S P H E R E
C I           S   R
U N           S   I
U A           E   C
M T           R   A
  S O U N D       L
  R
```

### Across

1. _____
6. _____
7. _____

### Down

2. _____
3. _____
4. _____
5. _____

Applications

# 7B  Description of the Moon

*Directions*: Match the surface features listed below with their locations on the moon.
Some blanks may have more than one answer.

a.  Montes Alpes
b.  Montes Apenninus
c.  Crater Alphonsus
d.  Montes Carpathius
e.  Montes Caucasus
f.  Crater Copernicus

g.  Montes Haemus
h.  Montes Jura
i.  Mare Crisium
j.  Mare Fecunditatis
k.  Mare Frigoris
l.  Mare Imbrium

m.  Mare Nectaris
n.  Mare Serenitatis
o.  Mare Tranquilitatis
p.  Oceanus Procellarum
q.  Crater Plato
r.  Crater Ptolemaus

s.  Montes Pyrenaeus
t.  Crater Tycho
u.  Largest mare
v.  Spectacular crater
with rays extending
over 1600 km

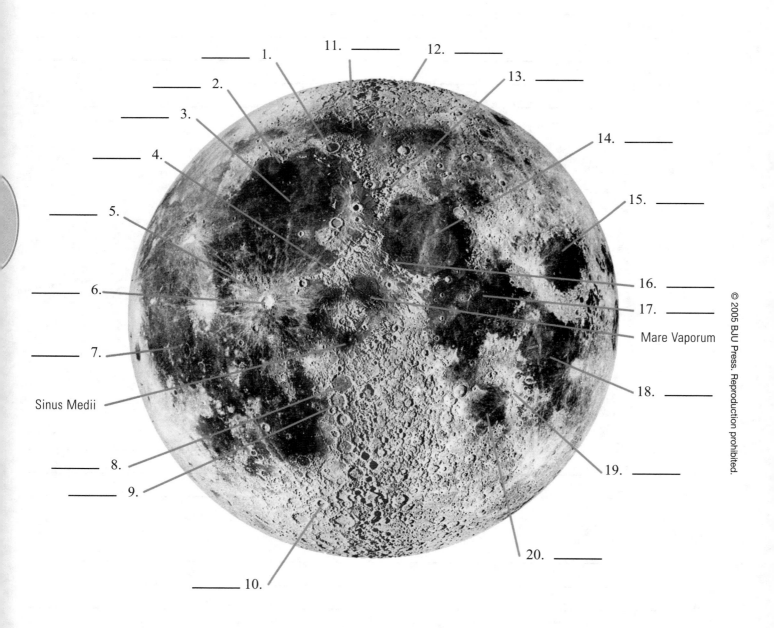

Applications

# 7C The Moon's Motions

*Directions*: Below are several diagrams or statements concerning the phases of the moon. Read each question carefully and write the answer in the space provided.

1. Name the moon phase represented in each diagram (*S* = Sun, *E* = Earth, *M* = Moon).

   a. _____  b. _____  c. _____  d. _____

  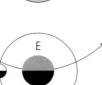  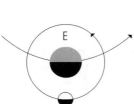   

2. What positions could the moon occupy during the new moon phase that does *not* result in an eclipse?

   _____

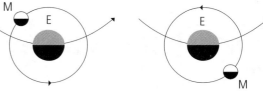

3. In the following diagrams the darkened areas represent the shadowed side of the moon. Decide the phase represented in each diagram and choose the sun position appropriate for that phase. Assume the view is from the Northern Hemisphere.

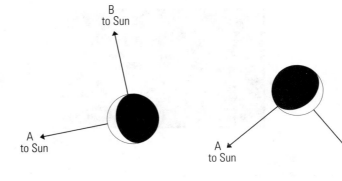

   a. Moon phase: _____    b. Moon phase: _____

   Correct sun position: _____    Correct sun position: _____

   How did the *shape* of the lighted area in these phases help you determine the sun's position?

   _____

4.  Identify the following phases as seen from your location.

a. _____     b. _____

5.  Draw the phase that occurs 22⅛ days into the lunar month as it would appear from your location.

6.  In the diagram below, *A* represents the sky and *B* represents the moon.

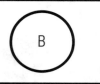

a.  During a full moon, which area is not illuminated? _____

b.  During a new moon, which area is not illuminated? _____

7.  Look at the diagram below and decide whether this view of the moon and sky is possible at your location. State why or why not.

   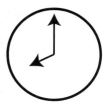

_____

_____

_____

_____

_____

Applications

# 7D  Features of the Moon

*Directions*: In each of the following statements, circle the correct choice in the parentheses.

1.  The (terminator / tropic) is the name of the line that divides the light and dark sides of the moon.

2.  During the first half of the lunar month, the moon is (waning / waxing). During the second half it is (waning / waxing).

3.  By the time the moon moves to the first quarter phase, the earth has rotated about (7 / 5) times.

4.  The hunter's moon occurs (one month / two months) after the harvest moon.

5.  During a (new / full) moon the far side of the moon is also the dark side.

6.  The length of the lunar month is (30 / $29\frac{1}{2}$) days.

7.  In the Northern Hemisphere the (harvest / hunter's) moon is the full moon that occurs nearest to the time of the autumnal equinox.

8.  Sunlight reflected from the earth to the moon and back to the earth is called (earthshine / moonshine).

9.  When the moon covers the planet Jupiter, an (eclipse / occultation) occurs.

10. The escape velocity of a rocket leaving the moon would be (lower / higher) than that of one leaving the earth.

11. The point in the moon's orbit where it is closest to the earth is called the (perigee / perihelion).

# 7E  Eclipses

*Directions*: Match the images on the right with the proper choices on the left. The answer spaces represent the number of possible answers for each image. Use each letter only once.

a.  Annular solar eclipse

b.  Baily's beads

c.  Corona

d.  Diamond ring effect

e.  Lunar eclipse

f.  Moon too distant to cover the whole solar disk

g.  Partial solar eclipse

h.  Sunlight shining through craters around the moon's edge

i.  Total solar eclipse

j.  Moon passes into the earth's shadow

_____, _____ 1.

_____ 2.

_____ 3.

_____, _____ 4.

_____, _____ 5.

_____, _____ 6.

Investigation
# 7F  Determining the Moon's Distance

The moon is mentioned throughout the Bible in a variety of ways: as the "lesser light" to rule the night, as a symbol of authority in one of Joseph's dreams, as an indicator of seasons, as a symbol of a woman's beauty, as a testimony to the length of Christ's millennial reign, and as an omen of judgment in the last days. David gives perhaps the most important lesson that a person can learn by considering the moon. He wrote a poem (Ps. 8:3–4, 9) expressing how amazed he was that God, who created such a wonder, could care at all about tiny, insignificant man. All David could say was, "O Lord our Lord, how excellent is thy name in all the earth!"

## Goal
Determine the distance from the earth to the moon.

## Materials
index card, 3 in. × 5 in.
hole punch
stapler
spring clip
meter stick
ruler
calculator

## Setting Up
1. On an index card draw the 4 cm by 7 cm rectangle pictured below.

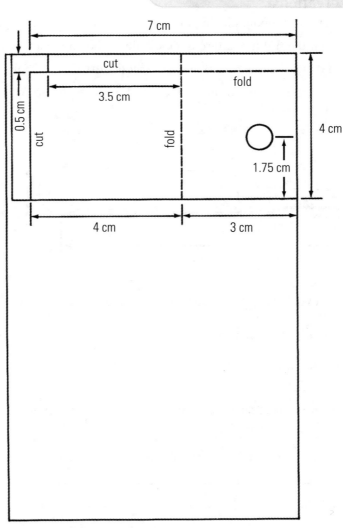

2. Cut on the solid lines and fold on the dotted lines.

3. Punch a hole with a hole punch where indicated above. Measure the diameter of the hole: _____mm = $d_{hole}$

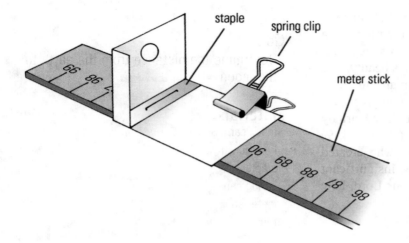

## Procedure and Observations

1. Aim the meter stick at a full moon, placing the 0 cm end just below your eye.

2. Close one eye and sight the full moon through the hole of the clip attachment.

3. Slide the clip up and down the meter stick until the moon just fills the hole.

4. Measure the distance in millimeters from the 0 cm end of the meter stick to the far edge of the sighting hole assembly.

$r_{hole}$ = _____ mm

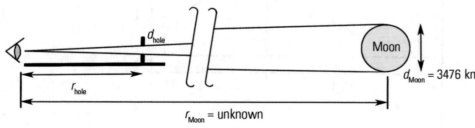

## Summing Up

1. The formula given below allows you to calculate the distance (in kilometers) to the moon:

$$\frac{r_{Moon}}{d_{Moon}} = \frac{r_{hole}}{d_{hole}} \quad \text{or} \quad r_{Moon} = d_{Moon} \times \frac{r_{hole}}{d_{hole}}$$

$r_{Moon}$ = _____ km

2. According to your answer Question 1, how many miles away is the moon? (1 km = 0.6214 mi.)

_____

3. According to your book, what distance from the earth in kilometers is the moon at its perigee? _____

At its apogee? _____

4. According to your calculations, would you say that the full moon you observed is closer to its apogee or to its perigee?

_____

5. When the moon is close to the horizon, it appears larger. Can you think of a reason that this is so?

_____

Investigation

# 7G  The Moon's Orbital Speed

## Procedure

1. Assume that the moon's orbit is circular with a radius of 385,000 km (the moon's average distance from the center of the earth).

2. Calculate the circumference of the moon's path, using the formula $C = 2\pi r$. (Use the pi key on your calculator or use the value $\pi = 3.1415$.)

   _____

3. Multiply twenty-four hours by 27.33 days (the moon's true orbital period) to obtain the total number of hours needed for one revolution.

   _____

4. Divide the total distance (step 2) by the total time (step 3) to obtain the moon's average orbital speed. Round your answer to the nearest hundred kilometers per hour.

   _____

> ### Goal
> Calculate the moon's average speed in kilometers per hour.
>
> ### Materials
> calculator

## Summing Up

1. Is your answer accurate? Why or why not? _____

   _____

   _____

2. Since the moon's orbit is not perfectly circular, the moon will travel faster at some places than at others. Where will it travel faster, at its apogee or its perigee?

   _____

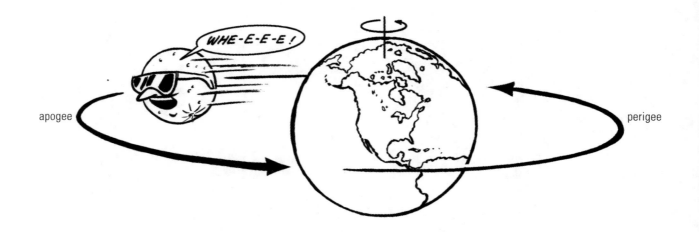

# 7H Mapping the Moon

No study of the moon is complete without a direct observation of it. In this investigation you will make a map of the moon, not from diagrams, photographs, or models, but from your observation of the moon itself.

## Procedure

1. Set up your telescope on a clear night when there is a full moon and focus on the moon.

2. Without using the telescope, draw and shade in any lunar features (maria, mountains, and craters) that you see on the diagram of the moon on the next page.

3. View the moon through the telescope. Draw in on your diagram other details you can see. You may need to adjust the telescope occasionally as the moon moves out of the field of view.

4. The diameter of the moon is 3476 km; the diameter of your drawing is 15 cm. Use the proportion below to determine how many kilometers 1 cm of the diameter of your drawing represents. Round to the nearest kilometer.

$$\frac{x}{1 \text{ cm}} = \frac{3476 \text{ km}}{15 \text{ cm}}$$

For the diameter of your drawing, 1 cm represents

_____ km.

5. Using the map of the moon on page 150, label the maria, mountains, and craters that you drew on your map.

6. The labeled points on your diagram indicate the locations of the Apollo landings. They are in no particular order. Match the letter with the correct Apollo mission number and landing site name.

### Goal

Make a map of the moon.

### Materials/Requirements

full moon on a clear night
telescope or binoculars
pencil

| Letter | Name | Landing Site |
|---|---|---|
| _____ | *Apollo 11* | Mare Tranquilitatis |
| _____ | *Apollo 12* | Oceanus Procellarum |
| _____ | *Apollo 14* | Fra Mauro (south of Crater Copernicus) |
| _____ | *Apollo 15* | Hadley Rille (near Montes Apenninus) |
| _____ | *Apollo 16* | Crater Descartes |
| _____ | *Apollo 17* | Taurus-Littrow (southeast of Mare Serenitatis) |

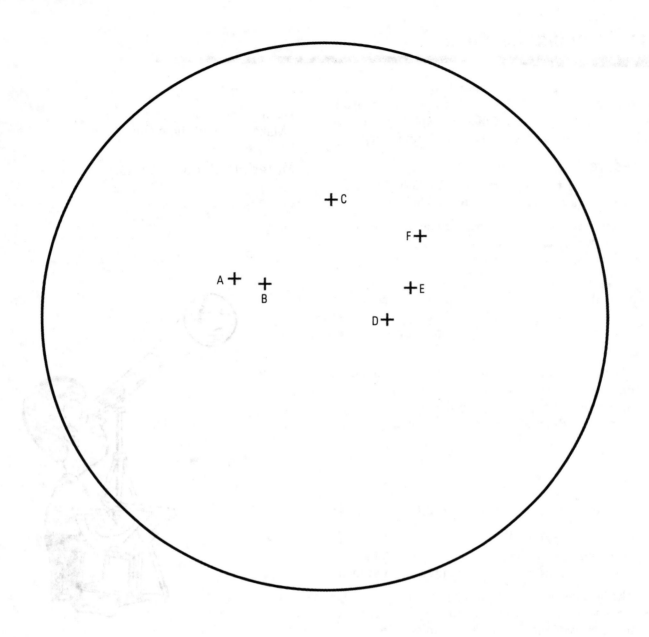

## Summing Up

1. Was the image you viewed with the telescope right-side-up or upside-down from the way the moon appears in the sky?

   _____

2. What is the general name for the large dark areas you shaded? _____

3. How did the conditions on the earth interfere with your view of the moon? _____

   _____

4. Why did you have to adjust the telescope due to the moon's movement? _____

   _____

   _____

5. Why do you think Mare Tranquilitatis was chosen as the landing site for the first Apollo landing? _____

   _____

Investigation

# 71 The Moon's Phases

## Setting Up

1. Find a clear area on the floor several meters across, and place an *X* in the center with masking tape.

2. Place one end of the meter stick at the center of the *X*.

3. Mark the meter stick with a piece of tape at 33 cm from the end at the *X*.

4. Using a protractor, rotate the meter stick around the *X* in 45° increments, and place tape markers on the floor at 33 cm and 1 m at each position. The eight markers at 33 cm will represent the position of a person on the earth's surface as it rotates. The eight markers at 1 m will represent the positions of the moon in its orbit.

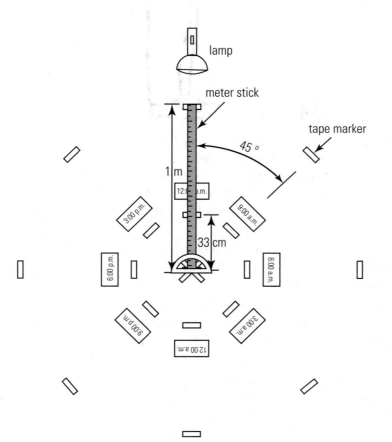

5. Place the light source directly in line with (but well outside of) one set of the two marks on the floor.

6. Use index cards to make time labels as shown in the figure, and tape them to the floor. Be sure the 12:00 noon card is in line with the initial position of the light source.

# Procedure

1.  Your teacher will assign someone to follow the path of a person on the "earth's surface" and someone to carry the "moon" (volleyball) in its orbit.

2.  The person on the "earth" should stand facing the "sun" (the light source) on the mark on the inner circle that is closest to the "sun." The "earth observer" should always face out.

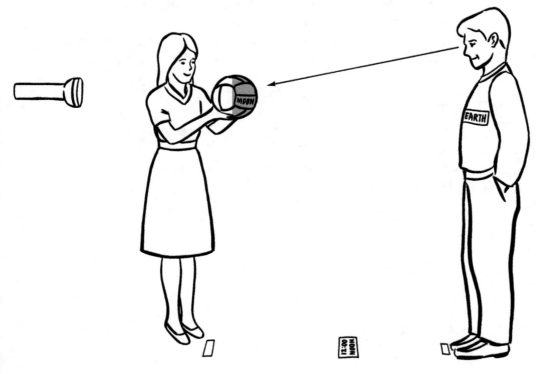

3.  The person carrying the "moon" should hold the "moon" directly over the 1 m mark between the "earth" and the "sun," making sure his shadow does not interfere with the "sun's" illumination of the "moon." At all other positions the person carrying the "moon" should hold the "moon" over the position marker in a similar way. Ensure that the ball label or fill valve always faces the "earth" and hold the ball at the height of the observer's eyes.

4.  In order to simulate the near-parallel rays of the sun, the lamp should be repositioned for each moon position so that the light rays are always parallel to the original direction of the light. (See the diagram on page SA109.)

5.  The observer on the "earth" should darken the appropriate circle in the Observations section to make it look like his view of the "moon." A "full moon" should be shown by a blank circle; a "crescent moon" should be darkened except for a tiny sliver.

6.  After observing the "moon's" phase and while the "moon" remains in the same position, the "earth" observer should extend both of his arms to form the "horizon". His left hand is the eastern horizon and his right hand is the western horizon. He should step in a counterclockwise direction from marker to marker to simulate the rotation of the earth, making sure that he always faces out. Any time the "moon" is in front of his extended arms, the "moon" is above the horizon. If the "moon" is behind his arms, then it has set and is not visible. When the observer on the "earth" returns to the original marker, he will have rotated *once.* In the Observations section, record the name of the moon phase that was observed and the rising and setting time for that phase.

7. When the "earth observer" has rotated through all the positions once, the "moon" should move counterclockwise to the next position. This position represents about 3½ days into the lunar cycle.

8. Repeat steps 5 and 6 for each of the eight marked positions of the "moon."

## Observations

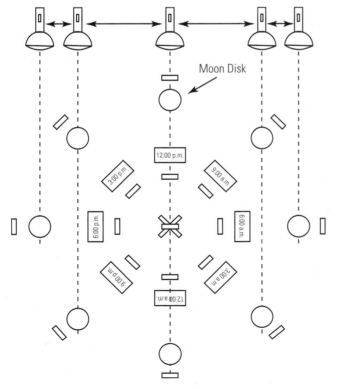

Moon Disk

12:00 p.m.

3:00 p.m.     9:00 a.m.

6:00 p.m.     6:00 a.m.

9:00 p.m.     3:00 a.m.

12:00 a.m.

| | Phase | Time that moon rises | Time that moon sets |
|---|---|---|---|
| 1. | | | |
| 2. | | | |
| 3. | | | |
| 4. | | | |
| 5. | | | |
| 6. | | | |
| 7. | | | |
| 8. | | | |

## Summing Up

1. Is only one-quarter of the "moon" illuminated during the "first-quarter moon"? _____
   _____
   _____

2. What does the word "quarter" mean in the term *last quarter*? _____
   _____

3. Did the "moon" rotate in its path? If so, how many times? _____
   _____

4. During what phase is a lunar eclipse possible? _____

# 8 SPACE EXPLORATION

Applications
## 8A Rocket History

*Directions*: Match the rocket design to the right with the following statements by placing the proper letter in the blanks provided.

_____ 1. Most primitive gunpowder rocket

_____ 2. Used by both the United States and the USSR to develop ICBMs

_____ 3. Introduced the gyroscopic guidance system

_____ 4. Used the long-stick guidance system

_____ 5. First to use spin for better accuracy

_____ 6. Used by the Germans late in World War II

_____ 7. Earliest liquid-fuel rocket

_____ 8. Used more often as fireworks than for military purposes

_____ 9. Used extensively by the nineteenth-century military

_____ 10. Liquid-fuel rockets with the longest range

> C—Chinese "flying fire" rocket
> G—Goddard rocket
> H—Hale rocket
> V—Wernher von Braun "V-2" rocket

Applications
## 8B Satellite Orbits

*Directions*: Below are three diagrams of satellites in orbit. Examine each carefully, and answer the questions in the spaces provided.

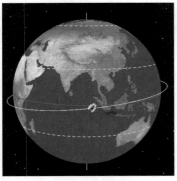

1. Name of orbit: _____

2. Definition: _____
   _____
   _____

3. What type of satellite would be especially adapted to this type of orbit?
   _____

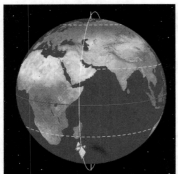

4. Name of orbit: _____

5. Definition: _____
   _____
   _____

6. What type of satellite would be especially adapted to this type of orbit?
   _____

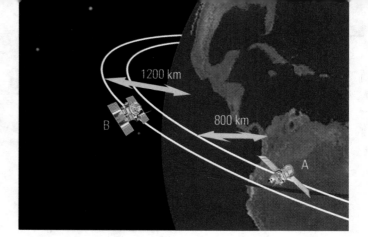

7. Which satellite orbit will take longer to complete?

_____

8. Which satellite is moving faster? _____

Applications

# 8C  Space Programs

*Directions*: In the table below are several categories of space projects. Each category is followed by three columns. Fill in the blanks with the appropriate information. (Hint: Look at the information that is already given to get an idea of what is needed.)

| Category | Type | Use | Examples |
|---|---|---|---|
| **Satellites** | (1) | used mainly for scientific studies | *Explorer I*<br>(2) |
| | (3) | (4) | Navstar series, GPS, GOES, etc. |
| **(5)** | Sounding Rockets | used for vertical probes of the atmosphere | V-2, *Scout*<br>(6) |
| | (7) | | (8) |
| | Planetary Probes | (9) | (10)<br>(11) |
| | (12) | used to explore specific objects in space such as comets, asteroids, etc. | (13)<br>(14) |
| **Manned Space Projects** | Early Efforts | man in orbit | (15) |
| | | man on the moon | (16) |
| | | space stations | (17) USSR:<br>(18) USA: |
| | Modern Efforts | space stations | (19) USSR:<br>(20) 16 partners: |
| | | shuttle orbiters | (21) |
| | | commercial and recreational | (22) |

Applications
# 8D Man in Space

*Directions*: Listed below are the accomplishments of various people who have contributed in some way to our knowledge of space. In each of the following statements, circle the correct choice in the parentheses.

1. (Yuri Gagarin / Aleksei Leonov) was the first human in space.

2. The first American in space was (Alan Shepard / Ed White).

3. William Hale improved rocket guidance by replacing the wooden stick with a (gyroscope / finned nozzle).

4. (Neil Armstrong / Michael Collins) was the first man to walk on the moon.

5. Sir Isaac Newton formulated the (law of gravity / action-reaction law), which expresses the principle used by rockets.

6. Wernher von Braun helped in the development of German (V-2 / B-1) rockets.

7. The first woman in space was (Valentina Tereshkova / Sally Ride).

8. Robert H. Goddard has been called the father of the modern (rocket / missile).

9. John Glenn became the first American to orbit the (earth / moon).

10. Eileen Collins was the first female (space walker / shuttle pilot) in the American space program.

11. Yang Liwei was the first Chinese (-American astronaut / astronaut) to orbit the earth.

Applications
# 8E The Lunar Landing

*Directions*: Match the part of the Apollo spacecraft to the right with the statement that best describes it. For each statement write the proper letter in the blank provided. Some choices will be used more than once, and some statements will have more than one answer.

_____ 1. Traveled all the way to the surface of the moon

_____ 2. Controlling station while in moon orbit

_____ 3. Left behind on the moon

_____ 4. Fell back to the earth once the spacecraft was in orbit

_____ 5. Upper stage of lunar module; docked with the command module

_____ 6. Housed the rocket engine to send the spacecraft back to the earth

_____ 7. Provided working and living quarters for the three-man crew

_____ 8. The stage of the lunar module that traveled from the moon back to the command module

_____ 9. Discarded just before the lunar astronauts re-entered the earth's atmosphere

_____ 10. Provided the thrust to move the spacecraft from the earth's orbit to the moon

_____ 11. The Apollo launch vehicle

_____ 12. The only section of Apollo flights to return to the earth

_____ 13. Never landed on the moon's surface but remained in lunar orbit

_____ 14. Designed to carry two astronauts to the moon's surface and return them to lunar orbit

_____ 15. Contained two stages

a. Ascent stage
b. Command module
c. Descent stage
d. Lower booster stages of Saturn V
e. Lunar module
f. Saturn V
g. Service module
h. Upper booster stage of Saturn V

## Investigation

# 8F Forces and Balloon Rockets

Nearly 400 years ago, the brilliant English physicist Sir Isaac Newton discovered three basic laws of motion that all typical objects obey. He discovered that all motion and changes in motion were caused by **forces**. A force is a push or a pull on an object, exerted by something else. Briefly, the three laws of motion are as follows:

**First Law:** An object in motion will remain in motion in a straight line and at the same speed unless acted on by an unbalanced force.

**Second Law:** An unbalanced force on an object will cause it to accelerate (change its speed).

**Third Law:** If an object is acted on by a force, it will push back in the opposite direction with an equal force.

*Balanced forces* means all forces acting on an object at the same time cancel each other out. An *unbalanced force* means that one of the forces acting on an object is stronger than the others. Unbalanced forces cause a change in motion.

Most forces that you are aware of are exerted by direct contact, such as the force to shut a door or the force of a bat on a baseball. Other forces do not require contact to have an effect. Examples of noncontact forces are gravity and magnetism. Whenever a force is exerted, all three laws of motion apply. However, in this investigation, you will be mainly interested in Newton's third law.

Imagine that you are on roller skates standing next to a wall. Your weight is a force acting downward on the floor. The floor pushes back with an equal force to hold you up. This is an example of Newton's third law. When you push against the wall, you roll backwards. You pushed on the wall and the wall pushed against you. This is also the third law of motion. Since you could move and the wall couldn't, the unbalanced force that the wall exerted caused you to move (you were accelerated—Newton's second law of motion).

A rocket in space, or even in the air, cannot physically push against any solid object. But Newton's laws of motion still apply. This is how a rocket works.

1. Fuel burns in the rocket combustion chamber of the rocket engine. (See the diagram.) The hot gases expand and press against the sides of the combustion chamber with great pressure.

2. The sides of the combustion chamber, which are part of the rocket, push back against the gas pressure to keep it contained (Newton's third law).

## Goal

Demonstrate Newton's third law of motion: the action-reaction law.

## Materials

calculator
stopwatch
large drinking straw
tape measure (a 5 m or 10 m tape is best)
masking tape
balloon, long cylindrical kind
fishing line, 10 m
paper clips of equal size, 2

3. Part of the combustion chamber is a nozzle, a small opening where the hot, high-pressure gases are allowed to escape. The unbalanced force of the gas pressure accelerates the exhaust gases through the nozzle (Newton's second law).

4. The escaping exhaust gases push back on the gases in the combustion chamber, which push against the rocket (Newton's third law). This unbalanced force causes the rocket to accelerate (Newton's first and second laws).

Notice that the rocket never has to push on any external object or substance in order to accelerate.

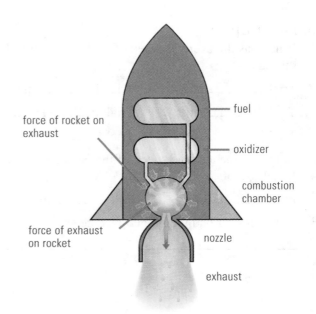

force of rocket on exhaust

fuel

oxidizer

combustion chamber

force of exhaust on rocket

nozzle

exhaust

## Setting Up

1. Tie or tape one end of the fishing line to the back of a chair.

2. Pass the free end of the line through the straw.

3. Tie the free end of the line to another chair on the opposite side of the room. Move the chairs slowly apart until the line is taut.

4. Inflate a balloon to about half its volume and pinch the end shut with your fingers. To estimate half the volume, you can measure the length of the inflated portion of the balloon.

5. Have your partner unbend two paper clips and tape them to the inflated balloon as shown in the following figure.

6. Move the straw all the way to one end of the line.

7. Hook the free ends of the paper clips over the straw as shown. The paper clips should grip the straw, but not so tightly as to cause drag on the string.

## Procedure and Observations

1. When your partner says "Go," you should release the balloon, and he should start the stopwatch. He should stop the stopwatch when the balloon stops.

2. Measure the distance covered by the balloon.

3. Repeat the procedure two more times (for a total of three trials), using the same balloon each time.

4. Record the length of time (in seconds) and the distance (in meters) of each run.

   Trial 1: time _____ s       distance _____ m

   Trial 2: time _____ s       distance _____ m

   Trial 3: time _____ s       distance _____ m

5. Repeat steps 1 through 5 of the procedure, but this time inflate the balloon to near its full volume. Record time and distance for each trial below.

   Trial 4: time _____ s       distance _____ m

   Trial 5: time _____ s       distance _____ m

   Trial 6: time _____ s       distance _____ m

## Summing Up

1. What was the average speed of each run? (*Hint*: Divide the distance by the time of the run.)

   Trial 1: _____ m/s        Trial 4: _____ m/s

   Trial 2: _____ m/s        Trial 5: _____ m/s

   Trial 3: _____ m/s        Trial 6: _____ m/s

2. Calculate the average speed of the partially inflated balloon rocket and the fully inflated rocket.

   Partial: _____ m/s        Full: _____ m/s

3. Which rocket had the higher average speed? _____

   _____

4. Describe all of the factors and observations that were different between the two balloon rockets.

_____

_____

_____

_____

5. Which of the factors described in Question 4 was the most important in producing the change in motion of the rocket?

_____

_____

_____

_____

6. Predict what would happen if you could double the amount of air in the full balloon without breaking it. Explain your prediction.

_____

_____

_____

_____

7. What other forces were acting on the balloon and straw (the moving parts of the rocket) during the run?

_____

_____

_____

_____

## Investigation
# 8G Model Rocket Project

Building and launching a model rocket is an exciting and challenging activity. This investigation will help you better understand the characteristics of the action-reaction principle.

## Procedure
### PART A: BUILDING THE ROCKET

Your rocket kit includes complete directions for finishing your rocket. Read the kit instructions and this procedure fully before beginning. Your teacher will clarify what must be done if there are differences between the two sets of instructions. Consider the following helpful tips as you complete your rocket project:

1. Inventory your kit before you start any kind of work on it. This helps you become familiar with the terminology, parts of the kit, and the directions.

2. The engine block is a small cardboard ring that keeps the engine from blowing right through the rocket. If you have trouble finding it, look inside the rocket tube.

3. Fin alignment guides are sometimes printed on the instruction sheet or on the back side of the cardboard insert of the rocket kit. If your kit calls for this guide, be sure to keep the cardboard insert. A plain piece of paper cut from a pattern from someone else's model will work as well.

4. Sand the balsa wing parts only enough to produce the correct shape specified in the instructions. Note that both surfaces of each wing must be rounded the same or the fin could cause the rocket to fly erratically.

5. After the balsa parts are shaped, sanding sealer is applied to keep the paint from being soaked up by the wood. Be very careful to not apply the sealer to the surfaces that will be glued to the rocket tube. When dry, lightly sand the surfaces to obtain a smooth finish.

6. Your teacher will probably keep the glue in a central location. Get only a small amount at a time on a small square of aluminum foil, and use a plastic or wooden stick to apply it.

7. Glue the fins in place using the fin alignment guide. Set the rocket aside to dry thoroughly.

## Goal
Build and launch a model rocket.

## Materials
### For building your rocket
model rocket kit (available from hobby and toy stores)
airplane glue (for plastic models)
white glue
rubber cement
wood splints for spreading glue
masking tape
spray paint (various colors)
mineral spirits or paint thinner for cleaning brushes
sanding sealer
paintbrush for applying sealer
sandpaper (fine grit)
single-edge razor blade
scissors, fine tip
aluminum foil
paper towels
piece of cardboard large enough to cover your desk
(other materials may be required by your kit)

### For launching your rocket
rocket engines (Your rocket-kit instructions will specify the size engine you need.)
extra igniters
launching pad and launcher (requires fresh batteries)
recovery wadding

8. When the glue is dry, it is time to paint the model. Your teacher will tell you whether there is enough time to create custom paint jobs with different color paints. Plan the pattern of colors and which colors you will use.

9. Painting needs to be done outside! Set up to spray paint well away from buildings, pavements, cars, or other people. Be careful to spray in the same direction the wind is blowing to keep paint off yourself.

10. Hold the paint can about 15–20 cm (6–8 in.) from the model, and move the can back and forth quickly to keep the paint from running. Several light coats are much better than one heavy coat. Ring stands make good holders for the rockets, although a long stick stuck in the ground will serve the same purpose.

11. If you are going to use other colors, wait until the first color is completely dry (usually 24 hours), then use masking tape to cover over the first color to create your pattern. Carefully spray the second color as before.

12. For water-based decals, you need a dish of water. Cut out the decal patterns carefully around the edge of the printed area. Place the decal under the water for about a minute. Carefully slide the decal off the paper backing onto the surface of the rocket. Blot dry with a paper towel. Do not wipe! Work very carefully when applying the decals to keep them from tearing.

13. If you lose the kit's launch lug (the tube that the launch pad rod uses to guide the rocket), a soda straw cut into small sections makes a good substitute. Use the launch pad as a guide when gluing the lug or soda straw in place.

## Part B: Launching the Rocket

1. Review the safety precautions with your teacher first.

2. Fit the engine into the engine mount of your rocket. The end with the ceramic nozzle should be toward the bottom of the rocket.

**Perform the following only when at the launch site—not in the classroom!**

3. Insert the igniter fully into the nozzle of the engine. Bend the wires slightly to the side and make sure they are not touching each other! Use a small piece of masking tape to secure the igniter in the engine.

4. Place the recovery wadding into the body tube of the rocket. Push it in until it is against the top of the engine. (This prevents the engine's recovery charge from burning the parachute or streamer.) Loosely wrap the parachute lines around the parachute (or loosely roll up the streamer) and push it into the body tube. Then fit the nose cone and its lanyard into the rocket. It should fit snugly.

5. Your teacher will have chosen a safe place and will have the launching equipment set up. When it is your turn to launch, slide the pole of the launcher through the launch lug of your rocket. Make certain that the safety key of the launcher is in place before you attach the clips to the igniters! Carefully attach the wires of the igniter to the clips of the launcher.

6. When your rocket is in place, check to make sure no one is standing close to the launch site. With your teacher's signal, have a countdown from 5 to 0. Then press the ignition button. Finally, enjoy retrieving your rocket!

## Summing Up

1. Why do you think it is important that the fins be properly aligned on a rocket? _____
_____

2. What is the purpose of the launch lug? _____
_____

3. When launching the rocket, why do you think it is important for the wires of the igniter not to be touching?
_____
_____

## Investigation
# 8H The Altitude and Speed of a Model Rocket

## Setting Up

1. Tape a protractor to a straw as indicated in the following figure. This will form the base of your clinometer.

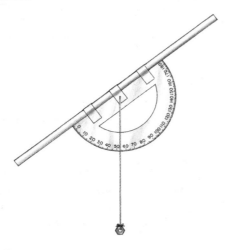

**Figure 1** The clinometer

2. Tie and tape a 30 cm piece of heavy black thread to the index (hole) of the protractor. It is important that the string comes through the hole on the side that the angle scale is read. This will form a plumb line.

3. Tie a small fishing sinker or machine nut to the free end of the string.

4. Hold the clinometer with the string on the right side of the protractor. (This investigation refers to the straw end closest to you as the *eyepiece* and the other end as the *far end*.)

## Procedure and Observations

1. The Observer should stand 100 m from the launching site with the clinometer.

2. The Timer should stand next to the Observer with a stopwatch.

### Goals
Use a clinometer to determine the altitude of a rocket.
Determine the speed of a rocket.

### Materials
large drinking straw
protractor
35 cm of black thread (heavy duty)
fishing sinker or machine nut
tape
rocket (assembled from a kit)
calculator (must have trigonometric function keys)
stopwatch

3. At the moment of launch, the Timer should start the stopwatch.

4. The Observer should follow the rocket by sighting through the eyepiece of the clinometer.

5. When the Observer sees the parachute deploy or the puff of smoke indicating the recovery charge fired, he should say "Now!" and immediately pinch the plumb line to the protractor.

6. The Timer should stop the stopwatch when the Observer says "Now!" How long was the flight?

_____

7. The Observer should read the smaller angle between the straw and the string pinched to the protractor. (See the previous figure.) What is the measurement of this angle?

_____

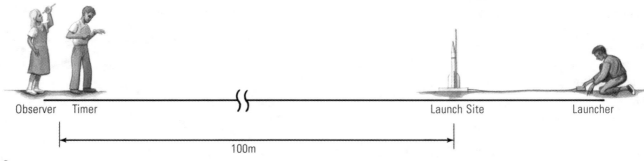

Observer    Timer                              Launch Site        Launcher

100m

**Figure 2**

## Summing Up

In order to determine the altitude of your rocket, you must use a special mathematical technique called *trigonometry*, although you could use a graphical method similar to the one used in the Investigation 3J. Your teacher will tell you which you should use. You can make the calculations using both methods and compare them.

Basic trigonometry involves right triangles. In a right triangle, the right angle always equals 90°. The other two angles can be any angle greater than 0° and less than 90°. These angles are called *acute* angles. The sum of the acute angles in a right triangle always equals 90°. In a right triangle, there are three sides—the *hypotenuse* (the longest side, which is opposite the right angle) and two shorter sides, called *legs*. The legs form the sides of the right angle. (See Figure 3.) Right-triangle trigonometry takes advantage of the fact that for a given acute angle measure, the ratio of the lengths of the legs is always the same. For example, with a 45° acute angle, the ratio of the opposite leg to the adjacent leg is always 1—the legs are the same length. The ratio of the opposite leg to the adjacent leg is called the *tangent* of the angle and is abbreviated "tan θ." The Greek letter *theta* (θ) is often used to represent an unknown angle.

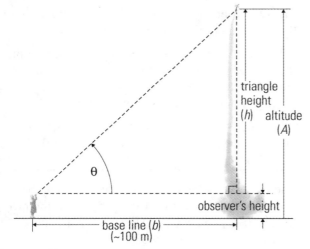

**Figure 3**  Right triangle diagram for calculating rocket height

In this investigation, you know the length of the adjacent side of a large right triangle. As in Investigation 2D, this line is called the base line. You determine the acute angle adjacent to the base line from the clinometer angle. The height of the rocket is the unknown length of the other leg.

From the definition of the tangent of an angle we can write the equation

$$\tan \theta = \frac{\text{opposite leg}}{\text{adjacent leg}} = \frac{h}{b}$$

where $h$ is the height of the triangle, $b$ is the length of the base line, and θ is the angle measured with the clinometer

subtracted from 90°. In order to solve for $h$, multiply both sides of the equation by $b$:

$$b \times \tan \theta = \frac{h}{\cancel{b}} \times \cancel{b},$$

Notice that the $b$s cancel on the right. The formula you will use to calculate the height of the rocket triangle is

$$h = b \tan \theta.$$

Use your calculator to find the tangent of the angle, then multiply the result by the length of the baseline in meters. The final answer will be the height of the rocket triangle in meters.

1.  Determine the altitude of the rocket.

    a.  Subtract the angle recorded in Step 7 of the Procedure from 90° to determine angle theta (θ).

    $$\theta = 90° - \text{reading}$$

    $$\theta = \underline{\hspace{2cm}}°$$

    b.  Compute the tangent of θ. If you are unsure of how to use your calculator, ask your teacher for assistance. Record the number to the fourth decimal place.

    $$\tan \theta = \underline{\hspace{2cm}}$$

    c.  Multiply the tangent of angle θ (Step 1b) by the length of the baseline (the Observer's distance from the launch pad). Unless your teacher says otherwise, this should be 100 m.

    $$\text{triangle height} = \text{base line} \times \text{tangent } \theta$$
    $$h = b \tan \theta$$
    $$h = (100 \text{ m})\tan \theta$$
    $$h = \underline{\hspace{2cm}} \text{ m}$$

    d.  The triangle height calculated is the height of the rocket above the Observer's head. The altitude ($A$) of the rocket is the height obtained in Step 1c plus the height of the Observer (in meters).

    $$\text{altitude } (A) = h + \text{height of the Observer}$$
    $$A = \underline{\hspace{2cm}} \text{ m}$$

2.  Determine the average speed of the rocket from the following formula:

    $$\text{average speed } (v) = \frac{\text{altitude, } A \text{ (meters)}}{\text{length of flight, } t \text{ (seconds)}}$$

    $$v = \frac{A}{t}$$

a. What is the average speed of the rocket in m/s?

_____ m/s

b. (optional) What is the average speed of the rocket in km/h?

$$x \, \frac{\text{m}}{\text{s}} \times \frac{1 \text{ km}}{1000 \text{ m}} \times \frac{60 \text{ s}}{1 \text{ min}} \times \frac{60 \text{ min}}{1 \text{ h}} = \underline{\hspace{1cm}} \text{ km/h}$$

3. List three factors that determine how high your rocket can go. _____

_____

_____

4. Does the speed that you calculated represent the rocket's maximum speed, or did it actually go faster or slower than that at some point in its flight?

_____

_____

5. Look at Figure 3. What assumption do you make about the position of the rocket compared to its launch pad when you measure the angle of its final position?

_____

_____

6. What would happen if the thrust of a rocket were exactly equal to the weight of the rocket?

_____

_____

7. What principle did you learn about in Investigation 8F that justifies your answer to Question 6?

_____

_____

## Go a Step Further

There are many interesting activities that can be done with rockets. The following are some ideas for further investigations.

1. Compare rocket weight to heights attained by the rockets in your class. After each flight, weigh the whole rocket including the spent engine. Plot the height and weight data on a graph to see if there is any relationship.

2. Experiment with different recovery parachute designs. Try different sizes of canopies, parafoils, multiple parachutes, and so forth. Measure the time from full deployment to landing on the ground. This is best done on a calm day. Graph the weight of the rocket assembly versus the duration the chute was open.

3. Set up two altitude-monitoring Observers similar to the one in this investigation's procedure. Have each team compute the altitudes independently and compare results.

# 9 INTRODUCTION TO METEOROLOGY

Applications

## 9A Composition of the Atmosphere

*Directions*: The diagram below represents the relative amounts of gases contained in the atmosphere. Label each area of the circle with the name of the gas that it represents. On the blank below the name, write the number representing the percentage of the total space that this gas occupies. Then answer the questions below the diagram.

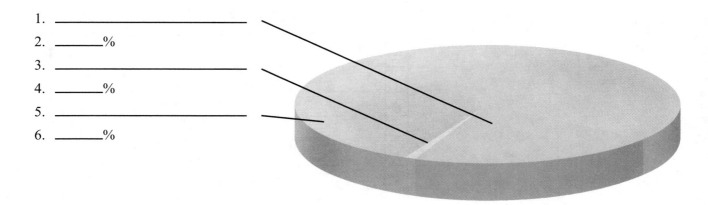

1. _____

2. _____%

3. _____

4. _____%

5. _____

6. _____%

7. List six other gases found in the atmosphere besides the ones you named above.

(1) _____  (4) _____

(2) _____  (5) _____

(3) _____  (6) _____

8. Who discovered oxygen? _____

9. Who discovered nitrogen? _____

Applications

# 9B Structure of the Atmosphere

*Directions*: Use the statements below to choose the right words to complete the word puzzle. All of the words deal with the atmospheric layers.

```
 1. __ __ __ __ __ __ │A│ __ __ __ __
 2.   __ __ __ __ __ __ │T│ __ __ __ __ __ __ __
 3.                 __ __ │M│ __ __ __ __ __ __ __ __ __
 4.           __ __ __ __ │O│ __ __ __
 5.   __ __ __ __ __ __ __ │S│ __ __ __
 6. __ __ __ __ __ __ __ __ │P│ __ __ __
 7.               __ __ __ │H│ __ __ __ __ __
 8.             __ __ __ __ │E│ __ __
 9.           __ __ __ __ __ │R│ __ __ __ __ __ __ __ __ __
10.             __ __ __ __ │I│ __ __ __ __ __ __ __ __ __
11.             __ __ __ __ │C│ __ __ __ __ __ __ __ __ __ __
12.             __ __ __ __ │L│ __ __ __ __ __
13.   __ __ __ __ __ __ __ │A│ __ __ __
14.             __ __ __ __ │Y│ __ __
15. __ __ __ __ __ __ __ __ │E│ __ __ __
16.     __ __ __ __ __ __ __ │R│ __ __ __ __ __ __ __
17.       __ __ __ __ __ __ │S│ __ __ __ __
```

1. Scientists divide the atmosphere into layers based on either gas composition or _____.

2. James Van Allen discovered the _____ by using satellites.

3. The temperature layer above the stratosphere is called the _____.

4. The _____ layer helps protect the earth from the sun's harmful ultraviolet light.

5. The second temperature layer, called the _____, is free of clouds and dust.

6. The temperature layer that helps vaporize meteors into "shooting stars" is called the _____.

7. _____ is a very common gas in the heterosphere.

8. High speed winds located in the stratosphere are called _____ streams.

9. The _____ is the only temperature layer that experiences a continual mixing of air.

10. Located within the thermosphere, the _____ is used by short-wave radio broadcasters to carry messages around the curve of the earth.

11. The homosphere and the heterosphere are divisions of the atmosphere based on gas _____.

12. In the troposphere the temperature drop that occurs with a given increase in altitude is called the _____ rate.

13. Charged particles from the magnetosphere sometimes escape high above the North Pole and collide with particles of the upper atmosphere, causing the aurora _____.

14. The troposphere is called the weather _____..

15. The _____ is a layer of uniformly mixed gases that surround the earth up to an altitude of 80 km.

16. Separate layers of hydrogen, helium, oxygen, and nitrogen make up the gas layer called the _____.

17. The top of the _____ contains the coldest temperatures in the atmosphere.

Applications

# 9C  The Atmosphere and Energy from the Sun

*Directions*: The sun's short-wave rays heat little of the earth's atmosphere. Not until the rays are absorbed by the earth and re-emitted as long-wave rays does the sun have much effect on the air. This indirect warming of the air is called the greenhouse effect. The diagram below describes the effect of the sun's energy on the earth and the atmosphere. Write the number from the diagram on the blank line next to the statement that best describes the process being illustrated.

_____ 1. The sun's rays (short-wave) travel through space toward the earth.

_____ 2. Outer gas molecules in the ionosphere absorb some of the sun's rays to produce ions.

_____ 3. The ozone layer filters out some of the sun's ultraviolet rays.

_____ 4. Clouds reflect some of the rays into space.

_____ 5. The air absorbs some of the rays of the sun.

_____ 6. The land and the water absorb the remaining rays of the sun.

_____ 7. As the land and water become heated, they give off long-wave radiation that heats the air.

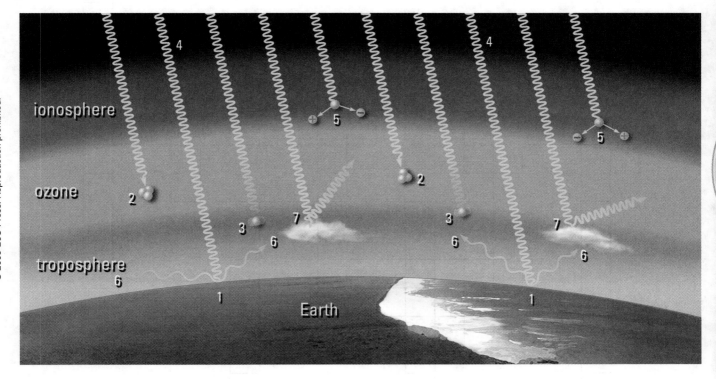

Applications

# 9D The Conditions of the Atmosphere

*Directions*: Complete the crossword puzzle below.

**Across**

2. Rain is the most common form of _____.

7. The atmospheric condition that is probably the first thing noticed on a clear day is _____.

8. _____ humidity is expressed as a percent.

11. Cool, dry air is usually a mark of _____ pressure.

13. The atmospheric condition that is caused by the weight of gases in the atmosphere is _____.

14. As air becomes warmer, it becomes less _____.

15. You will feel _____ on dry days than on humid days.

**Down**

1. The study of the lower atmosphere is called _____.

3. The apparent lowering of temperature by wind is called the wind _____ factor.

4. The condition of the atmosphere at any given time is called _____.

5. _____ air can hold more moisture.

6. At higher pressures water boils at a _____ temperature than at lower pressures.

9. _____ is greatly affected by the humidity; therefore comfort level is affected as well.

10. A wind traveling from west to east is called a _____ wind.

12. The amount of water vapor in the air is called _____.

## Investigation
## 9E The Effect of Temperature on the Volume of Air in a Balloon

### Procedure

1. Inflate a balloon and tie the end so that the air cannot escape. Do not inflate the balloon too much. If it is about 5 cm in diameter, it will be inflated sufficiently.

2. Measure the distance around the balloon (circumference). Record this on the table.

3. Immerse the balloon in the hot water and hold it under the water for about 60 seconds.

4. Remove the balloon from the water and quickly measure the circumference of the balloon again. Record this on the table.

5. Immerse the balloon in the ice water and hold it under the water for about 60 seconds.

6. Remove the balloon from the water and quickly measure the circumference of the balloon again. Record this on the table.

7. Repeat the procedure for trials 2 and 3. Calculate the average circumferences for all three trials.

### Goal
Demonstrate that warm air takes up more space than cold air.

### Materials
round balloon, at least 5 cm diameter
1 L beaker half-filled with hot water*
1 L beaker half-filled with ice water
cloth tape measure

*The water needs to be warm, but not so hot that the balloon bursts when inserted into it or that you risk injury.

|  | Trial 1 | Trial 2 | Trial 3 | Average |
|---|---|---|---|---|
| Circumference of balloon at room temperature |  |  |  |  |
| Circumference of balloon in hot water |  |  |  |  |
| Circumference of balloon in cold water |  |  |  |  |

### Summing Up

1. What could be said about the mass of the air in the balloon in every instance? _____

_____

2. What happened to the diameter of the balloon when the air inside was heated? _____

_____

3. What happened to the diameter of the balloon when the air inside was cooled? _____

_____

4. What general rule can you state regarding volume and temperature? _____

_____

5. When there is a change in density (because of the change in temperature), warm air will _____

because it is less dense, while cold air will _____ because it is more dense.

### Go a Step Further

1. Calculate the volume of the gas in each of the trials above if you have a spherical or nearly spherical balloon. The formula for the volume of a sphere is approximately

$$V = \frac{C^3}{59},$$

which is accurate enough for this demonstration. _____

Investigation

# 9F  The Effect of Air Pressure on Boiling Point

## Procedure

1. Set up the apparatus as shown below. The specific apparatus you are using may differ from what is shown.

2. Remove the stopper from the flask and pour in about 200 mL of warm tap water.

3. Insert the stopper and check that it fits snugly.

4. Turn on the faucet aspirator fully while holding the flask in your hand. If using a vacuum pump, your teacher will turn on the pump.

5. After a few minutes, what happens to the inside walls of the flask?

   _____

6. Eventually, if the aspirator can reduce pressure sufficiently, the water will begin to boil just as if it were in a pot on a stove.

### Goal
Demonstrate that reducing pressure lowers the boiling point.

### Materials
faucet aspirator or hand-operated vacuum pump
Florence flask, 500 mL
thick-walled rubber tubing, 30 cm length
one-hole stopper fitted with short glass tube
water
(optional) Ehrlenmeyer flask, 500 mL
(optional) two-hole stopper with glass tubing and thick-walled rubber hose
(optional) motor-operated vacuum pump

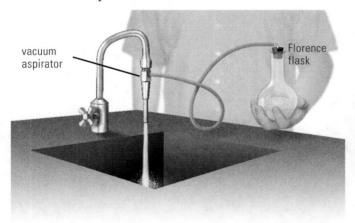

vacuum aspirator

Florence flask

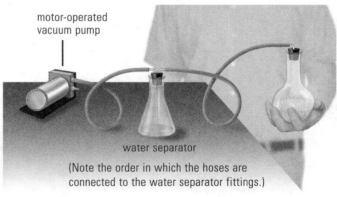

motor-operated vacuum pump

water separator

(Note the order in which the hoses are connected to the water separator fittings.)

## Summing Up

1. What effect does lowering the pressure have on the boiling point of a liquid? _____
   _____

2. What happens when more heat is added to a liquid at its boiling point—does it get hotter or does it boil faster?

   _____

3. Based on your answer to Question 2, would it take less time or the same amount of time to hard boil an egg if you used the high setting rather than the medium setting on the burner of your stove at home?

   _____

4. How would the amount of time to hard boil the egg on a high mountain compare to cooking the same egg at sea level? Explain your answer.

   _____
   _____
   _____

# 10 ATMOSPHERIC WATER

## Applications
## 10A Changes in State

*Directions*: Below is a list of terms that describe the changes in the physical states of water. Match each term with the statements that best describe it. Place the first letter of each term in the proper blank.

_____ 1. Cloud droplets change to hail.

_____ 2. Liquid water changes to water vapor without boiling.

_____ 3. Water vapor changes to frost.

_____ 4. Water vapor changes to dew.

_____ 5. Sleet changes to water.

_____ 6. Snow changes to water vapor.

_____ 7. Hail changes to rain.

_____ 8. Water vapor changes to clouds.

_____ 9. Dew changes to water vapor.

_____ 10. Rain changes to sleet.

| C | Condensation |
|---|---|
| E | Evaporation |
| F | Freezing |
| M | Melting |
| S | Sublimation |

## Applications
## 10B Precipitation

*Directions*: In each of the following statements, circle the correct choice in parentheses.

1. (Condensation / Coalescence) is the building up of raindrops by the combining of many smaller drops.

2. (Freezing rain / Sleet) occurs when supercooled water falls as rain and freezes on everything it touches.

3. (Sleet / Hailstones) are round chunks of ice that form from large rain droplets that freeze in clouds containing strong updrafts.

4. Most snow crystals are (six-sided / three-sided).

5. All forms of moisture falling from the atmosphere are called (precipitation / condensation).

6. (Freezing rain / Sleet) is formed when rain falls through a layer of cold air.

7. (Drizzle / Freezing rain) occurs when small droplets of water fall slowly.

8. (Snowflakes / Sleet) form(s) when supercooled water freezes around clay or dust particles.

9. (Dew / Frost) forms when a cool surface such as a plant leaf or automobile windshield comes in contact with a humid air mass.

10. If the dew point is below freezing and the object is cold enough, (frost / dew) may form.

# 10C Types of Clouds

*Directions*: Complete the cloud table on the following page, using the diagram below.
Be as complete as possible with your description in the space given.

name: _____

date: _____ hour: _____

| Number from diagram | Cloud name | Altitude zone | Altitude (in km and mi) | Symbol | Description |
|---|---|---|---|---|---|
| 1 | | | | | |
| 2 | | | | | |
| 3 | | | | | |
| 4 | | | | | |
| 5 | | | | | |
| 6 | | | | | |
| 7 | | | | | |
| 8 | | | | | |
| 9 | | | | | |
| 10 | | | | | |

Investigation
# 10D Evaporation and Condensation

## Setting Up

1. Soak the sponges for 1 minute in water so that they are thoroughly saturated.

2. Set up the meter stick and balance support with the sponges attached so that they balance as shown in the diagram.

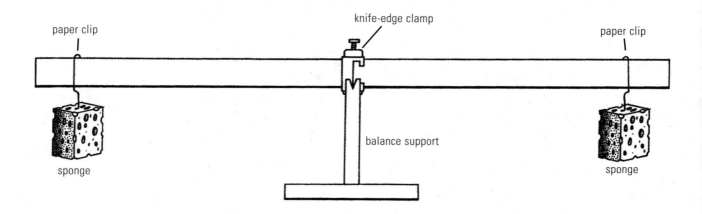

## Procedure

1. Test for the effect of various factors on the rate of evaporation as follows:

   a. *Wind*: Set up the fan or hair dryer on low speed so that it blows across one of the sponges for 2 minutes. Observe. (If no visible effect is noticed in the balanced apparatus, allow the fan to continue to blow until the effect is seen.)

   b. *Heat*: Resoak the sponges and rebalance them. This time place the heat source under one of the sponges (keep it far enough away to avoid overheating the sponge). Observe after 2 minutes. (As above, allow more time if necessary.)

   c. *Humidity*: Resoak the sponges and rebalance them. Suspend one sponge in a beaker that has about an inch of water in the bottom of it. Do not allow the sponge to touch the water or the sides of the container. Allow time for evaporation and observe.

   d. *Nature of the evaporating substance*: Wring out both sponges so that they are as dry as possible. Blot with paper towels. Soak one sponge in water and the other in rubbing alcohol. Allow 2 minutes for evaporation to occur and observe. (Allow more time if necessary.)

### Goals
Examine conditions that affect evaporation.
Demonstrate the processes of evaporation and condensation.

### Materials
meter stick
meter stick knife-edge clamp and support base
beaker, 500 mL
rubbing alcohol (enough to soak one of the sponges)
paper clips, 2
sponges (5 cm ×10 cm each), 2
paper towels
hair dryer or small fan
watch or clock
heat source (hot plate or stove burner)
ice cube
large watch glass or shallow bowl large enough to cover beaker
water

2. Demonstrate the processes of evaporation and condensation.

   a. Add about 250 mL of water to the beaker and place it on the hot plate over medium heat.

   b. Place the watch glass on top of the beaker.

   c. Place an ice cube in the watch glass.

   d. Observe.

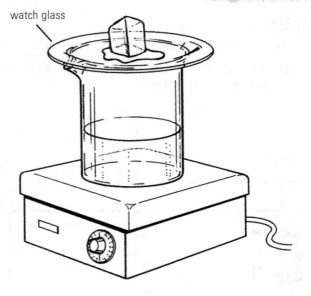

watch glass

## Summing Up

1. What effect did moving air have on the rate of evaporation? _____
   _____

2. What effect did heat have on the rate of evaporation? _____
   _____

3. What effect did humidity have on the rate of evaporation? _____
   _____

4. Do some substances evaporate more quickly than others? _____
   How do you know? _____
   _____

5. What other factors do you think might affect the rate of evaporation? _____
   _____
   _____

6. In the second part of the investigation, where was evaporation taking place? _____
   _____

7. Where was condensation taking place? _____
   _____

8. Was melting taking place? _____ Explain. _____
   _____

9. Was sublimation or freezing taking place? _____ Explain. _____
   _____
   _____

Investigation

# 10E Measuring Dew Point

## Procedure and Observations

1. Fill a shiny metal can half full with water that is near room temperature.

2. Record the air temperature on the thermometer.

   _____ °C

3. Place the thermometer into the water in the can. After a minute, record the water temperature.

   _____ °C

4. Remove the thermometer. Add ice, one piece at a time, and stir gently with a stirring rod. **Do not stir with the thermometer!**

5. Remove any ice as soon as you can see condensation on the outside of the can. Measure and record the temperature of the water.

   _____ °C

   If the water cools to 0 °C and no dew appears on the sides of the can, add rock salt to the ice water mixture to further reduce the temperature (the ice must be colder than 0 °C for this to be successful). If the dew point is below freezing, frost will appear on the sides of the can.

### Goal
Measure the temperature at which condensation occurs (the dew point).

### Materials
shiny metal can or glass
water
laboratory thermometer (−20 °C to 110 °C or similar)
stirring rod
ice (directly from freezer)
rock salt

6. Remove the thermometer and stir the water until the dew disappears. Measure and record the temperature of the water.

   _____ °C

7. If the temperatures recorded in steps 5 and 6 differ by more than 3°, repeat Steps 4–6. If they are within 3° of each other, find their average. This is the dew point.

   Dew point = _____ °C

## Summing Up

1. What is a dew point? _____
   _____

2. Was the initial temperature of the water (Step 3) above or below the dew point (Step 7)? _____
   _____

3. Would you expect the dew point on a rainy day to be different from the dew point
   on a cool, clear day? _____
   Why? _____
   _____

4. According to your text, what is frost, and when does it occur? _____
   _____

5. According to your text, when do fog and clouds form? _____
   _____

## Investigation
# 10F Cloud Formation

## PART 1

Clouds form when the temperature of a humid air mass decreases below its dew point. In this investigation, you will make a mass of warm, humid air meet a mass of cold air to prove this.

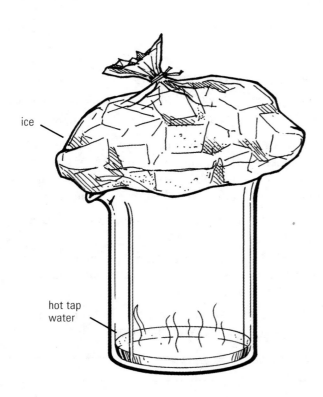

ice

hot tap water

### Goal
Demonstrate cloud formation by allowing a warm, humid air mass to meet a cold air mass.

### Materials
beaker, 1 L (or large-mouth quart jar)
hot tap water
ice (directly from freezer)
plastic bag

### Procedure and Observations

1. Pour about 50 mL of hot tap water into the beaker.

2. Fill the plastic bag with ice cubes or crushed ice straight from the freezer.

3. Set the plastic bag on top of the beaker.

4. After several minutes, observe to see whether a cloud has formed.

5. Observe after several more minutes. Is the cloud at the same elevation in the beaker?

_____

_____

_____

## Summing Up

1. Where did the warm, humid air mass in the beaker come from? _____

_____

2. How did you decrease the temperature of the warm, humid air mass? _____

_____

3. Under what conditions would you expect the temperature of a warm, humid air mass in the atmosphere to decrease?

_____

_____

_____

# PART 2

When water vapor condenses, clouds form. You will use alcohol vapor to make a "cloud." In order to make the alcohol vapor (gas state) change to a cloud (liquid state), you must lower its temperature. You can accomplish this by compressing the alcohol vapor and then letting it expand suddenly. Compressing the gas raises its temperature, and letting it expand lowers its temperature.

## Goal
Demonstrate cloud formation by condensing alcohol vapor.

## Materials
alcohol (rubbing or isopropyl), 30 mL
large-mouth quart jar
large, heavy latex balloon
rubber band
wooden safety match

## Procedure and Observations

1. Pour 30 mL of alcohol into the large-mouth jar.

2. Cut a 15 cm square of latex from the balloon.

3. Light the match, then blow it out. Lower the still-smoldering match into the bottle, then remove it. This provides smoke particles that will serve as nuclei on which the alcohol vapor can condense.

4. Stretch the latex sheet across the mouth of the jar. Secure it with the rubber band.

5. After 10 minutes, *slowly* push the center of the rubber sheet in several centimeters with your finger or a blunt object.

6. Hold the latex sheet in for 10 seconds and then release it suddenly. What happens?

_____

_____

## Summing Up

1. Was the alcohol vapor contracting or expanding when you released the latex sheet? _____

_____

2. What happened to the temperature of the alcohol vapor when you pushed in on the latex sheet?

_____

3. What happened to the temperature of the alcohol vapor when you released the latex sheet?

_____

4. What physical principal causes temperature to decrease when the volume of a gas increases with no energy input?

_____

5. Into what state did the alcohol vapor change when you released the latex sheet? _____

_____

6. What physical state is a vapor? _____

# 11 MOVEMENT IN THE ATMOSPHERE

Applications

## 11A Air Masses and Fronts

*Directions*: Listed below are several statements concerning air masses and fronts. Complete the statements by filling in the missing words in the spaces provided.

1.  When different air masses meet, boundaries are formed called _____.

2.  A warm front occurs when a _____ air mass overtakes a _____ air mass.

3.  Warm fronts generally produce a widespread, steady _____.

4.  When warm air replaces cold air, a _____ front results.

5.  When cold air replaces warm air, a _____ front results.

6.  Cold fronts often produce _____.

7.  If the boundary between two air masses is not moving, the front is called _____.

8.  A _____ _____ is a line of violent thunderstorms.

9.  _____ air masses are warmer than the surfaces over which they pass.

10. _____ air masses are cooler than the surfaces over which they pass.

Applications

## 11B Air Masses

*Directions*: Match each air mass below with the statements that best describe it. Place the abbreviation for each air mass in the proper blank; then complete the questions below.

_____ 1.  Originates over the North Atlantic

_____ 2.  Originates over the Caribbean

_____ 3.  Originates over the extreme northern parts of Canada

_____ 4.  Brings dry, warm weather

_____ 5.  Originates near the equatorial Pacific

_____ 6.  Brings humid and cool or cold air

_____ 7.  Originates near the equatorial Atlantic

_____ 8.  Brings dry, clear, cool, or cold conditions

_____ 9.  Brings humid, cloudy, hot, or mild weather

_____ 10. Originates over the South Pole

_____ 11. Originates over Mexico

| cA | continental arctic |
| cT | continental tropical |
| mT | maritime tropical |
| cP | continental polar |
| mP | maritime polar |

12. Which source regions are land masses? (Use the choices above.) _____

13. Which two source regions are large bodies of water? (Use the choices above.) _____

Applications

# 11C Global Wind Patterns

*Directions*: Listed below are various descriptions of wind belts. Match the correct descriptions with their proper names by placing the numbers of the descriptions on the spaces provided to the right of the diagram. Some wind belts may have more than one correct description.

After you have completed the matching section, draw the directions of the wind belts on the globe below. Draw solid-line arrows to represent those winds originating from the east and dotted-line arrows for those originating from the west.

Polar northeasterlies _____

Prevailing southwesterlies _____

Northeast trades _____

Southeast trades _____

Prevailing northwesterlies _____

Polar southeasterlies _____

1. Located just above the equator, these winds move from the northeast to the southwest.

2. Located near 30° S, these winds flow from the northwest to the southeast.

3. Located near 30° N, these winds flow from the northeast to the southwest.

4. Located just below the equator, these winds move from the southeast to the northwest.

5. Located near the South Pole, these winds come from the southeast.

6. Located near the North Pole, these winds travel to the southwest.

7. Located near 30° N, these winds flow from the southwest to the northeast.

8. Located near the North Pole, these winds come from the northeast.

9. Located near 60° N, these winds come from the southwest.

10. Located near the South Pole, these winds travel to the northwest.

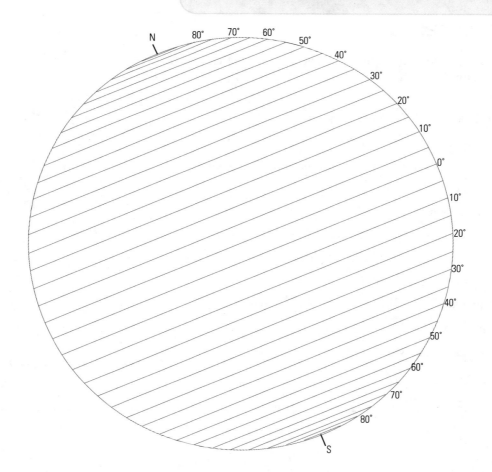

Applications
# 11D High- and Low-Pressure Zones

*Directions*: Listed below are five statements concerning high- and low-pressure belts. In the spaces provided, write *True* if a statement is true and *False* if a statement is false.

_____ 1. Air moves from high-pressure to low-pressure zones on the earth.

_____ 2. The earth's high- and low-pressure zones remain in the exact same locations all year long.

_____ 3. Beginning at the North Pole and ending with the South Pole, every other pressure zone on the earth is a high-pressure zone.

_____ 4. Subsiding cold air causes the earth's high-pressure belts, and rising warm air causes the low-pressure belts.

_____ 5. The doldrums are located in two main areas on the earth—at 30° N and 30° S.

Applications
# 11E Lightning

*Directions*: Use the statements below to choose the right words for the blanks in the puzzle that follows. All of the words pertain to lightning.

1. A faint streamer, known as a stepped _____, heads downward from the cloud in steps.

2. Lightning is a(n) _____ discharge.

3. When the top of a cloud becomes positively charged, and the bottom becomes _____ charged, lightning occurs.

4. The _____, one of the three types of violent storms discussed in this chapter, is most commonly associated with lightning.

5. Lightning from distant clouds whose thunder you cannot hear is sometimes called _____ lightning.

6. The air along the path of a lightning bolt expands with an explosive force to produce the sound of _____.

7. When an atom or group of atoms acquires an electrical charge, the particle is called an _____.

8. A rapid series of flashes that travels up a stepped leader to the cloud is known as _____ strokes.

9. Lightning occurs within a cloud, between clouds, or between a cloud and the _____.

1. L __ __ __ __ __
2. __ __ __ __ __ __ I __ __ __
3. __ __ G __ __ __ __ __ __ __
4. __ H __ __ __ __ __ __ __ __ __ __ __
5. __ __ __ T __ __ __
6. __ __ __ N __ __ __
7. I __ __
8. __ __ __ __ __ __ N
9. G __ __ __ __

Applications

# 11F  Storms

*Directions*: Read the following statements and decide which of the types of violent storms are being described. Then indicate your answers by writing the proper letters in the blanks provided.

_____ 1. Called a cyclone in Australia

_____ 2. About 1000 occur in the United States each year

_____ 3. Has an "eye"

_____ 4. An electrical storm accompanied by heavy rains

_____ 5. About forty-four thousand occur on the earth each day

_____ 6. A narrow funnel cloud extending down from the source cloud

_____ 7. The most common type of violent storm

_____ 8. Called waterspouts when they occur at sea

_____ 9. Always originate over the ocean

_____ 10. The only real protection from these storms is evacuation

_____ 11. Forms an anvil-shaped cloud

_____ 12. Produces huge waves called storm swells far out at sea

_____ 13. Has an updraft that sometimes lifts roofs off buildings

_____ 14. Has a narrow path of destruction but great wind speed

_____ 15. Sometimes produces hail showers

_____ 16. Best protection from this is a specially designed storm cellar

_____ 17. Largest in size

_____ 18. Satellite photographs show loose spiral arms.

_____ 19. Loses energy as it passes over land

_____ 20. Often spawns many tornadoes

a. Thunderstorm
b. Tornado
c. Hurricane

Investigation

# 11G Solar Heating of the Earth

## Procedure and Observations

1. Cut out the pattern strips on page SA149 to make the solar heating device.

2. Glue the patterns onto cardboard and trim away the excess. Fold the strips at the appropriate places but do not tape them together.

3. With the shorter strip flat on the table, place a drop of wax from a burning candle at point *A*, another drop at point *B*, and a third drop at point *C*. The drops should be about the same size. Allow 5 minutes for the wax to harden before continuing.

4. Tape the ends of the strips together, and then tape the apparatus to a vertical surface as in the diagram below (right).

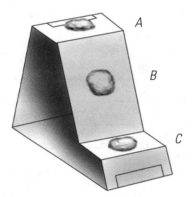

### Goal
Show the difference in heating effects between perpendicular and slanted solar rays.

### Materials
cardboard
glue
candle
matches
tape
scissors
solar heating device (see procedure)
newspaper, sheet
heat lamp
stopwatch

5. Place a sheet of newspaper directly below the apparatus to catch dripping wax.

6. Set up the heat lamp to shine on the solar heating device as shown. *Do not turn on the lamp at this time.* The lamp should be far enough away to keep the rays approximately parallel and close enough so that the wax will melt in the time allowed. This will depend on the wattage of the lamp. When the wax has melted it will begin to run.

7. Turn on the lamp. Observe the wax closely. Note the time when the wax forms a drop that begins to flow. Record the order in which the drops melt and the time it took (in seconds).

   a.  point *A* _____

   b.  point *B* _____

   c.  point *C* _____

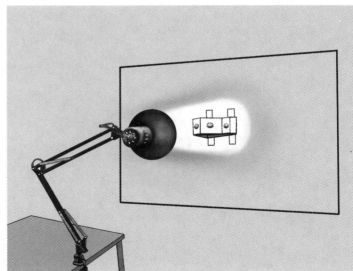

## Summing Up

1. The solar heating device has been designed so that if the rays are parallel, approximately the same quantity of heat will strike areas *A, B,* and *C.*

   a. What is the area of *A*? _____ cm²

   b. What is the area of *B*? _____ cm²

   c. What is the area of *C*? _____ cm²

2. If 800 joules of thermal energy are absorbed by each area, what is the density of energy in joules per cm² in each area?

$$\text{Energy density} \quad = \quad \frac{800 \text{ J}}{\text{area}}$$

   a. Area A: _____

   b. Area B: _____

   c. Area C: _____

3. Why did the wax melt earlier at certain points than at others? _____

   _____

   _____

4. Why did it take much longer to melt the wax at point *B*, even though it was closer to the heat lamp, than the wax at point *C*?

   _____

   _____

   _____

5. What could have caused the wax at point *A* to melt before the wax at point *C*? _____

   _____

   _____

   _____

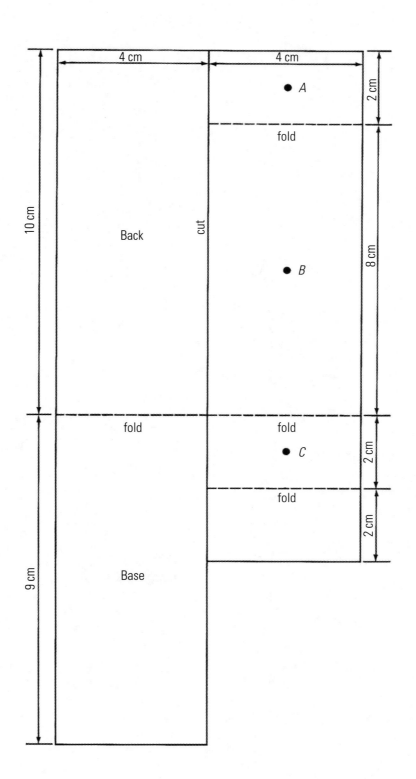

Investigation
# 11H Hurricane Tracking

An average of six tropical hurricanes per year occur in the North Atlantic area. Consequently, this area is referred to as the *Atlantic tropical cyclone basin*. It is only one of seven such tropical basins in the world.

A cyclone is any closed system in which winds rotate in a definite circular pattern (counterclockwise in the Northern Hemisphere and clockwise in the Southern Hemisphere). The term *tropical* refers to any cyclone that develops over tropical waters. Tropical cyclones, like other atmospheric circulation systems, pass through stages of development.

## Goal
Plot the paths of several hurricanes.

## Materials
colored pencils

| Stage of development | Wind speed (km/h) | Line style | Definition |
|---|---|---|---|
| tropical depression | ≤ 47 | •·······o | beginning (development) or ending stage of a warm-core tropical cyclone |
| tropical storm | 48–118 | •– – –o | middle stage of a warm-core tropical cyclone |
| category 1 hurricane | 119–153 | 1 | first or last stage of a warm-core tropical hurricane |
| category 2 hurricane | 154–177 | 2 | advanced stage of a warm-core tropical hurricane |
| category 3 hurricane | 178–209 | 3 | advanced stage of a warm-core tropical hurricane |
| category 4 hurricane | 210–249 | 4 | advanced stage of a warm-core tropical hurricane |
| category 5 hurricane | 250+ | 5 | most advanced stage of a warm-core tropical hurricane |

## Procedure and Observations

1. Plot the following information on the map on page SA155.

   a. Use open circles (o) for positions before noon, for example, at 6 a.m. (0600 UTC, the same as 0600 GMT) and closed circles (•) for positions at noon or later, such as 6 p.m. UTC (1800).

   b. Label each curve by placing the first letter of its name near the starting point. For example, *I* for Isabel, *J* for Jeanne, and so on. Use a different color for each storm.

   c. Connect the circles at each position with the appropriate line style to indicate the stage of development. For example, Jeanne changed from a tropical storm to a category 1 hurricane September 20 at 1800. Plot this information by putting a closed circle at the appropriate location with a number *1* over the point. Put a number over the point only when the hurricane strength changes. Connect points that plot a hurricane's movement with a solid line. Jeanne was rated as a tropical depression between September 13 at 1800 and September 14 at 0600. You will plot this information as a series of dots with a closed circle at one end and an open circle at the other end.

| Tropical cyclone | Date | Time (UTC) | Stage of development | Latitude (degrees) | Longitude (degrees) | Wind speed (km/h) |
|---|---|---|---|---|---|---|
| 1. Jeanne 2004 | Sept. 13 | 1800 | tropical depression | 15.9 N | 60.0 W | 46 |
| | Sept. 14 | 0600 | tropical depression | 16.3 N | 61.5 W | 56 |
| | Sept. 14 | 1800 | tropical storm | 16.7 N | 63.5 W | 93 |
| | Sept. 15 | 0600 | tropical storm | 17.2 N | 64.8 W | 102 |
| | Sept. 15 | 1800 | tropical storm | 18.1 N | 66.2 W | 111 |
| | Sept. 16 | 0600 | tropical storm | 18.6 N | 67.8 W | 111 |
| | Sept. 16 | 1800 | cat. 1 hurricane | 18.8 N | 69.0 W | 120 |
| | Sept. 17 | 0600 | tropical storm | 19.4 N | 69.9 W | 102 |
| | Sept. 17 | 1800 | tropical depression | 20.0 N | 71.6 W | 56 |
| | Sept. 18 | 0600 | tropical storm | 20.4 N | 72.5 W | 83 |
| | Sept. 18 | 1800 | tropical storm | 21.7 N | 72.3 W | 74 |
| | Sept. 19 | 0600 | tropical storm | 22.8 N | 72.3 W | 74 |
| | Sept. 19 | 1800 | tropical storm | 24.2 N | 72.3 W | 83 |
| | Sept. 20 | 0600 | tropical storm | 25.5 N | 72.0 W | 102 |
| | Sept. 20 | 1800 | cat. 1 hurricane | 27.2 N | 71.4 W | 139 |
| | Sept. 21 | 0600 | cat. 1 hurricane | 27.6 N | 70.2 W | 139 |
| | Sept. 21 | 1800 | cat. 1 hurricane | 27.4 N | 69.2 W | 139 |
| | Sept. 22 | 0600 | cat. 2 hurricane | 26.8 N | 68.7 W | 157 |
| | Sept. 22 | 1800 | cat. 2 hurricane | 26.2 N | 68.8 W | 157 |
| | Sept. 23 | 0600 | cat. 2 hurricane | 25.5 N | 69.3 W | 157 |
| | Sept. 23 | 1800 | cat. 1 hurricane | 25.8 N | 70.0 W | 139 |
| | Sept. 24 | 0600 | cat. 1 hurricane | 26.1 N | 71.2 W | 139 |
| | Sept. 24 | 1800 | cat. 2 hurricane | 26.4 N | 73.1 W | 157 |
| | Sept. 25 | 0600 | cat. 2 hurricane | 26.5 N | 75.6 W | 167 |
| | Sept. 25 | 1800 | cat. 3 hurricane | 26.9 N | 78.2 W | 194 |
| | Sept. 26 | 0600 | cat. 2 hurricane | 27.3 N | 80.6 W | 176 |
| | Sept. 26 | 1800 | tropical storm | 28.3 N | 82.3 W | 102 |
| | Sept. 27 | 0600 | tropical storm | 30.1 N | 83.3 W | 74 |
| | Sept. 27 | 1800 | tropical depression | 32.5 N | 83.6 W | 56 |
| | Sept. 28 | 0600 | tropical depression | 34.1 N | 82.4 W | 37 |
| | Sept. 28 | 1800 | tropical depression | 37.3 N | 78.4 W | 46 |
| | Sept. 29 | 0600 | extratropical | 38.8 N | 74.7 W | 65 |
| | Sept. 29 | 1800 | dissipated | — | — | — |

| Tropical cyclone | Date | Time (UTC) | Stage of development | Latitude (degrees) | Longitude (degrees) | Wind speed (km/h) |
|---|---|---|---|---|---|---|
| 2. Matthew 2004 | Oct. 8 | 1200 | tropical depression | 24.0 N | 95.4 W | 56 |
| | Oct. 9 | 0000 | tropical storm | 24.6 N | 93.7 W | 74 |
| | Oct. 9 | 1200 | tropical storm | 26.3 N | 92.8 W | 65 |
| | Oct. 10 | 0000 | tropical storm | 27.3 N | 91.4 W | 74 |
| | Oct. 10 | 1200 | tropical depression | 29.4 N | 90.9 W | 56 |
| | Oct. 11 | 0000 | extratropical | 32.0 N | 91.0 W | 46 |
| | Oct. 11 | 1200 | absorbed | — | — | — |
| 3. Isabel 2003 | Sept. 6 | 0600 | tropical storm | 13.9 N | 32.7 W | 64 |
| | Sept. 6 | 1800 | tropical storm | 13.4 N | 34.9 W | 82 |
| | Sept. 7 | 0600 | tropical storm | 13.9 N | 36.5 W | 110 |
| | Sept. 7 | 1800 | cat. 1 hurricane | 15.2 N | 38.5 W | 128 |
| | Sept. 8 | 0600 | cat. 2 hurricane | 16.5 N | 40.9 W | 174 |
| | Sept. 8 | 1800 | cat. 3 hurricane | 17.6 N | 43.1 W | 201 |
| | Sept 9 | 0600 | cat. 4 hurricane | 18.9 N | 45.2 W | 210 |
| | Sept. 9 | 1800 | cat. 4 hurricane | 20.0 N | 47.3 W | 210 |
| | Sept. 10 | 0600 | cat. 3 hurricane | 20.9 N | 49.4 W | 201 |
| | Sept. 10 | 1800 | cat. 4 hurricane | 21.1 N | 51.4 W | 220 |
| | Sept. 11 | 0600 | cat. 4 hurricane | 21.3 N | 53.2 W | 229 |
| | Sept. 11 | 1800 | cat. 5 hurricane | 21.5 N | 54.8 W | 265 |
| | Sept. 12 | 0600 | cat. 5 hurricane | 21.7 N | 56.6 W | 256 |
| | Sept. 12 | 1800 | cat. 5 hurricane | 21.7 N | 58.2 W | 256 |
| | Sept. 13 | 0600 | cat. 4 hurricane | 21.9 N | 60.1 W | 238 |
| | Sept. 13 | 1800 | cat. 5 hurricane | 22.5 N | 62.1 W | 256 |
| | Sept. 14 | 0600 | cat. 4 hurricane | 23.2 N | 64.6 W | 247 |
| | Sept. 14 | 1800 | cat. 5 hurricane | 23.9 N | 67.0 W | 256 |
| | Sept. 15 | 0600 | cat. 4 hurricane | 24.5 N | 68.8 W | 229 |
| | Sept. 15 | 1800 | cat. 4 hurricane | 25.3 N | 69.8 W | 210 |
| | Sept. 16 | 0600 | cat. 3 hurricane | 26.3 N | 70.5 W | 183 |
| | Sept. 16 | 1800 | cat. 2 hurricane | 27.4 N | 71.2 W | 174 |
| | Sept. 17 | 0600 | cat. 2 hurricane | 28.9 N | 71.9 W | 174 |
| | Sept. 17 | 1800 | cat. 2 hurricane | 30.6 N | 73.0 W | 165 |
| | Sept. 18 | 0600 | cat. 2 hurricane | 32.5 N | 74.3 W | 165 |
| | Sept. 18 | 1800 | cat. 2 hurricane | 35.1 N | 76.4 W | 156 |
| | Sept. 19 | 0600 | tropical storm | 38.6 N | 78.9 W | 91 |
| | Sept. 19 | 1800 | tropical storm | 43.9 N | 80.9 W | 54 |
| | Sept. 20 | 0600 | absorbed | — | — | — |

2. Which storm crossed over its own path? _____

3. What tropical storm passed over the Great Lakes? _____

4. Why did Matthew never become a hurricane? _____

_____

_____

_____

5. What made Jeanne finally dissipate? _____

_____

_____

_____

6. Which storm spent the most time in the eastern Atlantic? _____

7. What are the major differences between the three storms? _____

_____

_____

_____

_____

_____

8. Why do tropical cyclones not form closer to the equator than about 10 degrees north? Did these storms follow this rule?

_____

_____

_____

## Summing Up

1. What is a tropical basin? _____

_____

2. What is a cyclone? _____

_____

3. What is a tropical cyclone? _____

_____

4. What are the stages of a warm-core tropical cyclone? _____

_____

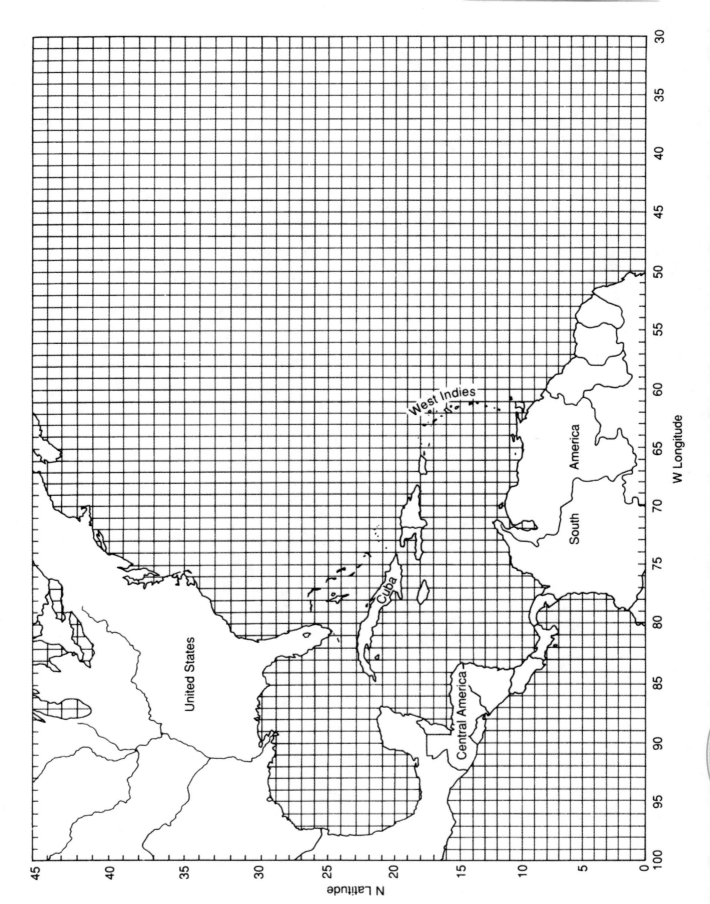

United States

Cuba

West Indies

Central America

South America

W Longitude

N Latitude

Investigation

# 11I Understanding Fronts and Air Masses

## Procedure

### PART I

1. Label the types of clouds (a–e).

2. Label the types of air masses (f, g).

3. Label the type of front (h).

4. Draw arrow tips on the lines (i, j) to indicate the direction that the air is moving.

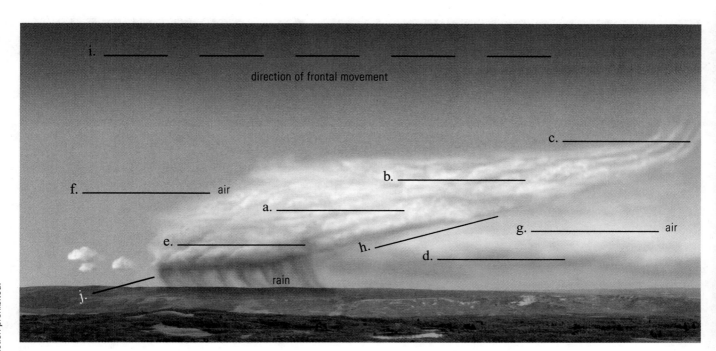

## PART 2

1.  Label the types of clouds (a–c).
2.  Label the types of air masses (d, e).
3.  Label the type of front (f).
4.  Draw arrow tips on the lines (g–i) to indicate the direction that the air is moving.

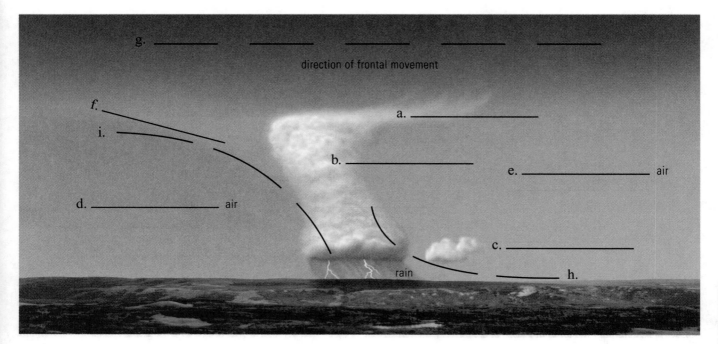

# 12 WEATHER PREDICTION

## Applications
## 12A Thermometers

*Directions*: Complete the table below comparing Fahrenheit and Celsius thermometers. Then answer the questions that follow.

|  | Celsius | Fahrenheit |
| --- | --- | --- |
| Inventor |  |  |
| Country introduced in |  |  |
| Fiducial points |  |  |
| Freezing point |  |  |
| Boiling point |  |  |
| Number of degrees between fiducial points |  |  |

1. Which thermometer is based on the metric system? _____
2. Convert 50 °F to Celsius. _____
3. Convert 50 °C to Fahrenheit. _____
4. Who invented the first device that measured temperature? _____
5. What liquid is in a maximum thermometer? _____
6. What liquid is in a minimum thermometer? _____
7. How does a Bourdon tube thermometer mounted indoors measure outdoor temperature? _____
8. What is the difference between a thermometer and a thermograph? _____
9. Why is the bottom of a thermometer shelter solid rather than containing air passages? _____
10. Why are the sides of a thermometer shelter latticed? _____

Applications

# 12B Barometers

*Directions*: Match the correct type of barometer with the following descriptions. In the space by each statement, place an *A* if it refers to an aneroid barometer or an *M* if it refers to a mercurial barometer.

_____ 1. Invented by Lucien Vidie

_____ 2. Invented by Evangelista Torricelli

_____ 3. Contains no liquid

_____ 4. Is very compact

_____ 5. Senses air pressure by being slightly collapsible

_____ 6. Easily converted to barographs

_____ 7. Constructed from a tubular glass column inserted into an open container at the bottom

_____ 8. Ideally suited for use in an airplane

_____ 9. Contains a liquid metal

_____ 10. Requires a complete vacuum to operate properly

Applications

# 12C Weather Measurement

*Directions*: Draw a circle around the correct choice in the parentheses for each of the following statements concerning weather instruments.

1. (Weather vane / Wind vane) is the correct name for the instrument that shows the direction of the wind.

2. Weather stations report wind speed in (miles per hour / knots).

3. Meteorologists use psychrometers to measure (relative humidity / specific humidity).

4. On a very dry day the (wet-bulb / dry-bulb) thermometer on a psychrometer will read lower because evaporation has taken place.

5. Older-model hygrometers and recording hygrometers used (animal / human) hair to measure relative humidity.

6. Pilot balloons measure wind speed at various (ground locations / altitudes).

7. Rain gauge readings are more accurate if the rainy period is relatively (windy / calm).

8. The (rawinsonde / pilot balloon) can function in all kinds of weather and at night.

9. Low-altitude weather satellites orbit the earth in (equatorial / polar) orbits. This orbit allows the satellites to view the entire earth within a twenty-four-hour period.

Applications

# 12D Station Model

## PART 1

*Directions*: Below is an example of a weather station model. Notice that there is an explanation for each entry in the model. Study the model carefully and then answer the following questions. Refer to Appendix A6 to obtain the meaning for each symbol.

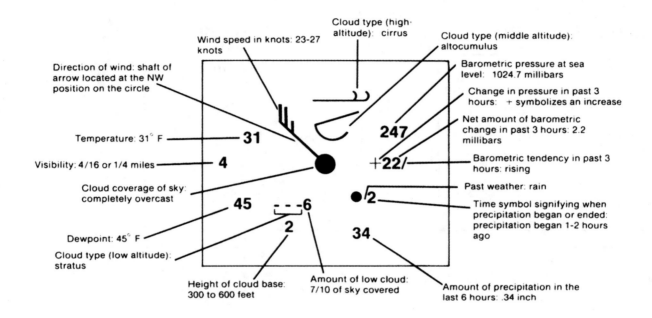

1. What do you notice about the location of cloud-type symbols on the model? _____

_____

2. What is the barometric pressure? How do you know? _____

_____

_____

3. If the symbol / represents a rising barometric pressure, what do you think ⌐ represents?

_____

4. If the shaft of the wind-speed arrow were located at the bottom of the circle, ⦁,
   what would be the direction of the wind?

_____

5. What is the wind speed of this symbol, ⧹⧹⧹ ?     _____ knots  _____ miles per hour

6. What is the wind speed of this symbol, ⌒ ?     _____ knots  _____ miles per hour

7. What does the symbol ◑ mean? _____

_____

8. Give all the information this symbol, ⦁⌒ , represents. _____

_____

_____

# PART 2

*Directions*: Below are four sample station models. Consulting Appendix A6, fill in the weather table on the following page for each model with all data that is shown on the sample station model. Not all information on the weather table will be filled in, since the station models do not address all of the conditions.

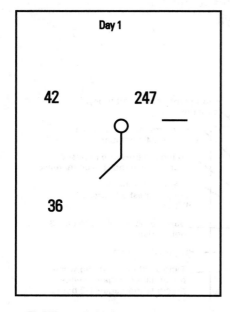

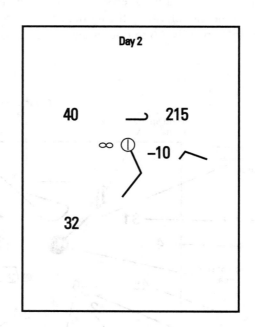

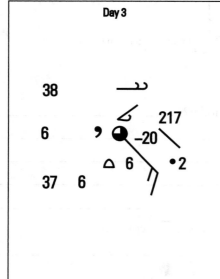

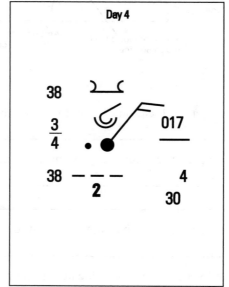

# WEATHER TABLE

| Condition | Day 1 | Day 2 | Day 3 | Day 4 |
|---|---|---|---|---|
| Temperature | | | | |
| Present weather | | | | |
| Visibility | | | | |
| Percent cloud cover | | | | |
| Dew point | | | | |
| Low cloud type | | | | |
| Middle cloud type | | | | |
| High cloud type | | | | |
| Height of cloud base (ft) | | | | |
| Amount of precipitation in last 6 h | | | | |
| Time precipitation began or ended; Past weather | | | | |
| Barometer reading | | | | |
| Barometer reading 3 h ago | | | | |
| Barometric tendency in past 3 h | | | | |
| Wind speed (knots) | | | | |
| Wind direction | | | | |

Applications

# 12E Weather Maps

*Directions*: Look at the weather map below. Use the legend to answer the following questions.

1. In which part of the United States is there a cold front? _____

2. Are there any stationary fronts? _____ If so, where? _____
   _____

3. In which part of the United States is there a warm front? _____

   In which direction is it moving? _____

4. In which part of North America is there a high-pressure system? _____
   _____

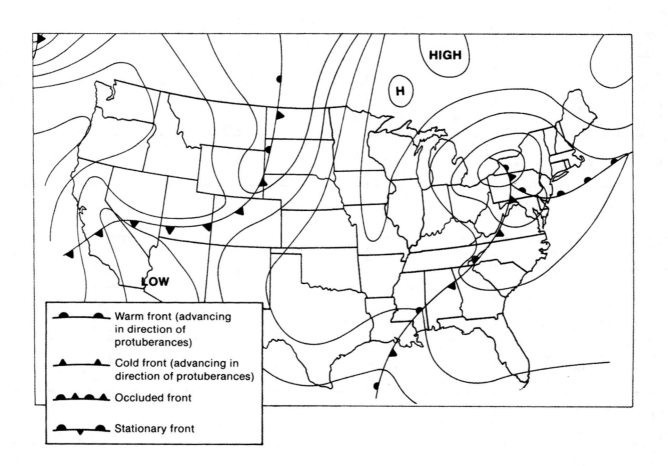

5. Excluding the fronts, what are the remaining weather-related lines on the map called? _____

6. Name a state where precipitation is probably occurring due to an occluded front. _____
   _____

Applications

# 12F  Isobars

*Directions*: Listed on the map are barometric pressure readings from various weather stations across the country. The readings are shown in millibars. Draw isobars to connect the stations that have the same barometric pressure. Closed isobars show the positions of high- and low-pressure areas.

The weather conditions associated with high-pressure areas are cool, clear, and fair; the low-pressure areas tend to bring warm, cloudy, changeable weather that is often accompanied by precipitation. On this map there are three main pressure areas. Identify these areas by writing either an *H* (high-pressure area) or an *L* (low-pressure area) where they occur.

Using the information given to you above, answer the following questions.

1. What do you think the weather was like in New York? _____
   _____

2. What do you think the weather was like in Oregon? _____
   _____

3. On this day (January 19) part of southeastern Colorado received 1 inch of snow. According to the barometric pressure readings in the area, was this precipitation likely or unlikely to occur? Explain why.

   _____
   _____

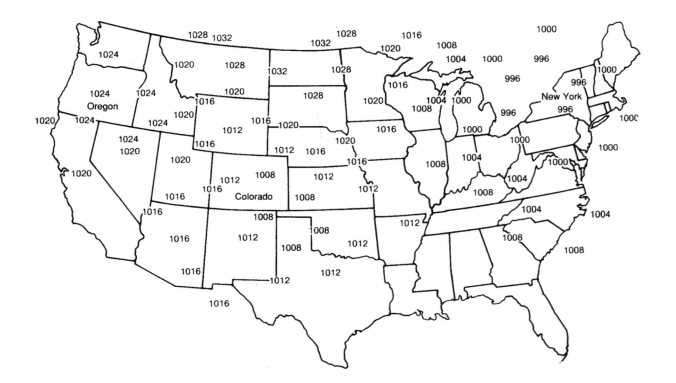

## Investigation
# 12G  A Simple Thermometer

In the early 1600s, Santorio, Galileo, and others worked together to develop the gas thermometer by following a process similar to what you will be doing in this investigation.

In order to calibrate thermometers, early scientists used two standard points that were easily defined—the freezing point of pure water (identical to the temperature of ice water) and the boiling point of water. These points are called *fiducial points* because they can be trusted to be the same anywhere in the world under the same conditions.

Because of the unequal rate at which water expands at low temperatures, early thermometers using water as an indicator were inaccurate at cold, near freezing temperatures. Of course, at temperatures below the freezing point of water, the thermometer was useless. Later thermometers used alcohol, which solved the problem of unequal expansion at cold temperatures. Alcohol, however, boils at relatively low temperatures (82 °C/179 °F). This low boiling point could cause a sealed glass tube to burst at temperatures well below the boiling point of water (100 °C/212 °F), and in open tubes the alcohol would vaporize.

Mercury came into use because it is a liquid at all points between the freezing and boiling points of water. Since mercury freezes at a relatively high temperature (−40 °C/−40 °F), alcohol thermometers are used to measure very cold temperatures, and mercury thermometers are used to measure high temperatures.

### Goal
Construct a simple thermometer.

### Materials
10–15 cm Pyrex test tube

1 hole rubber stopper (fits test tube)

6 mm glass or stiff plastic tubing, 40 cm long

food coloring

water

crushed ice

beaker, 250–300 mL

burner and beaker support stand or hot plate

test tube tongs

glass marker (overhead transparency pen or a sharp china grease pencil)

aluminum foil, 3 cm square

metric ruler

You will be using water because it is simple and safer to use than mercury or alcohol, and you will calibrate your thermometer with the same fiducial points used by the early scientists. Keep in mind that 0 °C (32 °F) on your thermometer will not be accurate because of the expansion properties of water near its freezing point. You will find, however, that your thermometer will work well enough for this investigation.

## Procedure

1. Insert the rubber stopper into the test tube to check that it will fit snugly.

2. Remove the stopper. Carefully insert the glass or plastic tubing into the stopper. (If you use glass, do so carefully! Lubricate the glass tube with water or special lab grease. Use a towel to protect your hand in case the glass tubing should break while you are inserting it into the stopper.) The tubing should go all the way through the stopper but should not extend out the bottom of the stopper (Figure A).

3. Add a few drops of food coloring to the test tube. Fill the test tube as full as possible with water.

4. Insert the rubber stopper and tubing into the test tube. The tubing should stick out of the test tube.

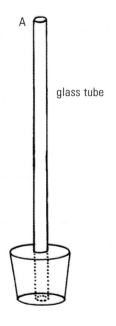

A

glass tube

5.  The colored water should rise up into the tubing several centimeters (Figure B).

6.  Fill a beaker with ice and add enough water to bring up the level of ice water in the beaker so that the test tube can be nearly immersed in the beaker of water (Figure C).

7.  Let the assembly stand in the ice water for about 5 minutes. After 5 minutes, mark the level of the water in the glass tube with a glass marker. (We will assume at this point that the water inside the test tube is the same temperature as the water in the beaker).

8.  Dump the ice water out of the beaker and fill the beaker with enough water so that that the test tube is fully immersed but not covered. Heat the water in the beaker until the water in the beaker begins to boil. Allow it to boil freely for about 2 minutes. Mark the level of the colored water in the tube at this point with the glass marker.

9.  Measure the distance between the two marks. Transfer the distance to a piece of paper. Divide the distance by ten and make marks so that there are equal divisions between your two marks. These division marks are approximately 10 degrees Celsius apart. Divide each division in half. These marks represent 5 degrees. If there is room, subdivide each half division into five equal parts. Number the scale from 0 to 100 in 10 degree increments.

10. Place an aluminum foil cap over the end of the thermometer tube to prevent the water from evaporating.

11. Tape your scale onto your thermometer tube so that you can read the temperature.

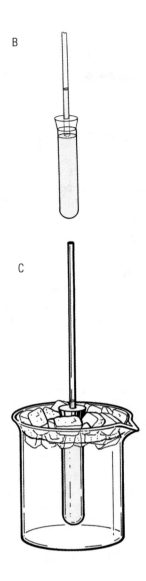

B

C

## Summing Up

1.  What is the temperature in the room where your thermometer is? _____

2.  Take your thermometer outside if the temperature is over 0 °C (32 °F). What is the outside temperature?
    _____

3.  Why is alcohol a better liquid for weather thermometers than water? _____
    _____
    _____
    _____

4.  Why are mercury thermometers not used as extensively as they once were? _____
    _____
    _____
    _____
    _____

5. Why is it important to have a cover over your thermometer? _____

_____

_____

6. Look up the word "fiducial" in a dictionary. Write the definition here. _____

_____

_____

_____

7. Why did you have to mark off ten divisions between the boiling and freezing points? _____

_____

_____

_____

8. How could you make your thermometer using a Fahrenheit scale? _____

_____

_____

_____

# 12H Making a Simple Barometer

Barometers, as you know, measure air pressure. Any pressure, including atmospheric pressure, is the force exerted over a given area. Units are written in terms of force per unit area, such as newtons per square meter ($N/m^2$) or pounds per square inch ($lb/in^2$ or psi). Somehow, a barometer must convert the force the atmosphere exerts on an area into something that changes in proportion to the force. Torricelli solved this problem by setting up a column of mercury in a closed glass tube immersed in a dish of mercury and measuring the height of mercury supported by the atmosphere. Vidie used a closed box containing a partial vacuum that flexed with changes of air pressure. In this investigation, you will construct a barometer using Torricelli's design as a basis, since it is simpler to construct.

## Procedure

It is necessary to make a partial vacuum in the bottle.

1. Fill the bottle with hot tap water.

2. Carefully insert the tubing through the stopper, leaving most of the length of the tubing extending out the wide end of the stopper. (If you use glass, do so carefully! Lubricate the glass tube with water or special lab grease. Use a towel to protect your hand in case the glass tubing should break while you are inserting it into the stopper.)

3. Pour the room-temperature water into the small cup. Add one or two drops of food coloring (optional).

4. Empty the hot water from the bottle, and quickly fit the stopper/tubing assembly into the bottle.

5. Invert the bottle and place the end of the tubing in the cup of water.

6. Secure the upside-down bottle with the ring-stand clamp while keeping the end of the tubing in the water.

7. As the air inside the bottle cools, it will contract, drawing some of the water up into the tubing. If the water rises too high in the tubing for the meniscus to be seen, repeat Steps 1–6, using warm water instead of hot water. Alternatively you could also allow a bubble of air to enter the tubing, reducing the vacuum and lowering the meniscus.

8. Allow twenty-four hours for the barometer to reach room temperature. If the water has risen too high in the tubing, see the suggestions in Step 7. Make a mark on the cup at the level of the water.

## Goal

Make a barometer to measure atmospheric pressure.

## Materials

insulated bottle, narrow mouth (thermos, etc.), 1 pint to 1 quart

hot tap water

rubber stopper, one-hole (large enough to fit in the mouth of the bottle)

glass or stiff plastic tubing (should fit the hole in the stopper), 30 to 40 cm

water, 50 mL, room-temperature

small cup

food coloring (optional)

ring stand with wide clamp (must be able to clamp vacuum bottle)

colored pencils, 2

graph paper

9. Temperature variations can affect the results of your barometer, so be sure to keep the barometer in an area with a fairly constant temperature. (Avoid direct sunlight or shelves near windows.)

10. Mark the level of the water in the tubing, and record the current barometric pressure from a calibrated barometer or current local weather report, such as from an airport, cable weather channel, or NOAA Weather Radio. Make several marks 1 cm apart above and below your current mark.

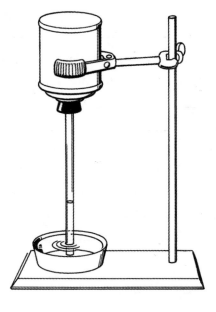

## Observations

1. Beginning on the day after you assembled the barometer, record the barometric reading every day for one week from your barometer and from a reliable source of actual barometric pressure (see Step 10 above). If the water level in the cup falls lower than the mark, add enough water to raise it to the original level before recording the barometric reading.

2. Graph your results. The horizontal axis will be for time. The vertical axis on the left side should be scaled for the pressure measurement taken from the reliable barometric pressure source. Plot this pressure using one colored pencil. The vertical axis on the right side will be scaled for the pressure measurement taken from your water barometer. Plot these pressures using the other colored pencil. Underline each axis label with the corresponding color.

| Day | Your barometric reading (mm$_{H_2O}$) | Actual barometric reading (mm$_{Hg}$) |
|-----|-----|-----|
| 1 | | |
| 2 | | |
| 3 | | |
| 4 | | |
| 5 | | |
| 6 | | |
| 7 | | |

## Summing Up

1. Does an increase in atmospheric pressure make the water level in the tubing rise or fall? _____

2. How did your pressure readings compare to those from a reliable barometric pressure source?

_____

3. Were there any changes in the weather during the week? How did they relate to your barometric readings?

_____

_____

4. What effect would an increase in room temperature, without a change in atmospheric pressure, have on your readings?

_____

_____

_____

_____

_____

_____

5. What would happen if the vacuum bottle lost its vacuum? Why?

_____

_____

6. What effect would using liquids with different densities (water, mercury, oil) in this type of barometer have on the readings?

_____

_____

_____

# 12I Measuring Relative Humidity

## Setting Up

Examine the diagram as you complete each step.

1. Drill holes in the top and bottom of each thermometer mounting. Make sure that the distances between the holes are exactly the same.

2. Screw two nuts onto the longer bolt.

3. Insert the short end of the bolt through the top hole of one thermometer mount from the front.

4. Place five washers over the short end of the bolt. Insert the bolt into the top hole of the second thermometer mount so that the two thermometers are back to back. Thread on two more nuts.

5. Screw two nuts onto the shorter bolt.

6. Slip the bolt from the front through the bottom hole of one thermometer mount.

7. Add five washers, slip the bolt through the second thermometer mount , and then thread on the last two nuts. Tighten the nuts in each pair against each other with two wrenches. This will keep the apparatus from flying apart in use.

8. Wrap the piece of gauze around the bulb of one thermometer. Bend the backing card slightly to perform this step, if necessary.

9. Use thread to secure the gauze to the thermometer.

## Procedure

1. Take your psychrometer, an eyedropper, and a cup of water outside. Allow the psychrometer to adjust to the outside temperature.

2. Fill an eyedropper with water from the cup and dampen the gauze on the "wet-bulb" thermometer.

3. Swing the psychrometer for one full minute. Read and record the temperatures in the table in the Observations section.

4. Repeat Steps 1–3 every day for a week. Be sure to measure the temperature at the same time each day.

5. Subtract the wet-bulb reading from the dry-bulb reading and record the difference under "Temperature Difference" in the Observations section for each day.

## Goal
Measure relative humidity with a psychrometer.

## Materials
Celsius thermometers (mounted on metal or stiff cardboard), 2  
5/32 in. drill bit and drill  
1/8 in. diameter bolts, one 2 in. long and one 6 in. long  
1/8 in. nuts, 8  
1/8 in. washers, 10  
gauze, 5 cm by 15 cm strip  
string or thread  
eyedropper  
cup filled with water  
daily weather report (dew point temperature)  
watch that displays seconds

6. Use the table on the next page to look up the relative humidity and record it on the observation chart. For example, if the wet-bulb reading is 13 °C and the dry-bulb reading is 27 °C, the temperature difference is 14 °C. Find the column "14.0" along the top row of the table (temperature difference), then drop down the column until you come to the "27°" row (dry-bulb temperature) to find the relative humidity (16%). This example is highlighted in the table.

7. Record the dew point temperature from your weather report each day.

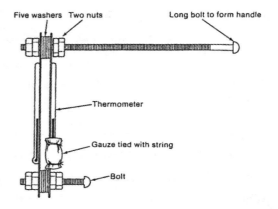

Five washers  Two nuts          Long bolt to form handle

Thermometer

Gauze tied with string

Bolt

## Relative Humidity (%)

### Differences between wet-bulb and dry-bulb temperatures (°C)

| Air temperature (dry bulb) (°C) | 0.0 | 0.5 | 1.0 | 1.5 | 2.0 | 2.5 | 3.0 | 3.5 | 4.0 | 4.5 | 5.0 | 5.5 | 6.0 | 6.5 | 7.0 | 7.5 | 8.0 | 8.5 | 9.0 | 9.5 | 10.0 | 10.5 | 11.0 | 11.5 | 12.0 | 12.5 | 13.0 | 13.5 | 14.0 | 14.5 | 15.0 |
|---|---|---|---|---|---|---|---|---|---|---|---|---|---|---|---|---|---|---|---|---|---|---|---|---|---|---|---|---|---|---|---|
| 0° | 91 | 81 | 73 | 64 | 55 | 46 | 38 | 29 | 21 | 13 | 5 | | | | | | | | | | | | | | | | | | | | |
| 1° | 92 | 83 | 75 | 66 | 58 | 49 | 42 | 33 | 25 | 17 | 10 | | | | | | | | | | | | | | | | | | | | |
| 2° | 92 | 84 | 76 | 68 | 61 | 52 | 45 | 37 | 29 | 22 | 14 | 7 | | | | | | | | | | | | | | | | | | | |
| 3° | 93 | 84 | 77 | 70 | 63 | 55 | 48 | 40 | 33 | 26 | 19 | 12 | 5 | | | | | | | | | | | | | | | | | | |
| 4° | 93 | 85 | 78 | 71 | 64 | 57 | 50 | 43 | 36 | 29 | 22 | 16 | 9 | | | | | | | | | | | | | | | | | | |
| 5° | 93 | 86 | 79 | 72 | 66 | 58 | 52 | 45 | 39 | 33 | 26 | 20 | 12 | 7 | | | | | | | | | | | | | | | | | |
| 6° | 93 | 86 | 80 | 73 | 67 | 60 | 54 | 48 | 41 | 35 | 29 | 24 | 17 | 11 | 5 | | | | | | | | | | | | | | | | |
| 7° | 94 | 87 | 81 | 74 | 68 | 62 | 56 | 50 | 44 | 38 | 32 | 26 | 21 | 15 | 10 | | | | | | | | | | | | | | | | |
| 8° | 94 | 87 | 81 | 75 | 69 | 63 | 57 | 51 | 46 | 40 | 35 | 29 | 24 | 19 | 14 | 8 | | | | | | | | | | | | | | | |
| 9° | 94 | 88 | 82 | 76 | 70 | 64 | 59 | 53 | 48 | 42 | 37 | 32 | 27 | 22 | 17 | 12 | 7 | | | | | | | | | | | | | | |
| 10° | 94 | 88 | 82 | 77 | 71 | 66 | 60 | 55 | 50 | 44 | 39 | 34 | 29 | 24 | 20 | 15 | 10 | 6 | | | | | | | | | | | | | |
| 11° | 94 | 89 | 83 | 78 | 72 | 67 | 61 | 56 | 51 | 46 | 41 | 36 | 32 | 27 | 22 | 18 | 13 | 9 | 5 | | | | | | | | | | | | |
| 12° | 95 | 89 | 84 | 78 | 73 | 68 | 63 | 58 | 53 | 48 | 43 | 39 | 34 | 29 | 25 | 21 | 16 | 12 | 8 | | | | | | | | | | | | |
| 13° | 95 | 89 | 84 | 79 | 74 | 69 | 64 | 59 | 54 | 50 | 45 | 41 | 36 | 32 | 28 | 23 | 19 | 15 | 11 | 7 | | | | | | | | | | | |
| 14° | 95 | 90 | 85 | 79 | 75 | 70 | 65 | 60 | 56 | 51 | 47 | 42 | 38 | 34 | 30 | 26 | 22 | 18 | 14 | 10 | 6 | | | | | | | | | | |
| 15° | 95 | 90 | 85 | 80 | 75 | 71 | 66 | 61 | 57 | 53 | 48 | 44 | 40 | 36 | 32 | 27 | 24 | 20 | 16 | 13 | 9 | 6 | | | | | | | | | |
| 16° | 95 | 90 | 85 | 81 | 76 | 71 | 67 | 63 | 58 | 54 | 50 | 46 | 42 | 38 | 34 | 30 | 26 | 23 | 19 | 15 | 12 | 8 | 5 | | | | | | | | |
| 17° | 95 | 90 | 86 | 81 | 76 | 72 | 68 | 64 | 60 | 55 | 51 | 47 | 43 | 40 | 36 | 32 | 28 | 25 | 21 | 18 | 14 | 11 | 8 | | | | | | | | |
| 18° | 95 | 91 | 86 | 82 | 77 | 73 | 69 | 65 | 61 | 57 | 53 | 49 | 45 | 41 | 38 | 34 | 30 | 27 | 23 | 20 | 17 | 14 | 10 | 7 | | | | | | | |
| 19° | 95 | 91 | 87 | 82 | 78 | 74 | 70 | 65 | 62 | 58 | 54 | 50 | 46 | 43 | 39 | 36 | 32 | 29 | 26 | 22 | 19 | 16 | 13 | 10 | 7 | | | | | | |
| 20° | 96 | 91 | 87 | 83 | 78 | 74 | 70 | 66 | 63 | 59 | 55 | 51 | 48 | 44 | 41 | 37 | 34 | 31 | 28 | 24 | 21 | 18 | 15 | 12 | 9 | 6 | | | | | |
| 21° | 96 | 91 | 87 | 83 | 79 | 75 | 71 | 67 | 64 | 60 | 56 | 53 | 49 | 46 | 42 | 39 | 36 | 32 | 29 | 26 | 23 | 20 | 17 | 14 | 12 | 9 | 6 | | | | |
| 22° | 96 | 92 | 87 | 83 | 80 | 76 | 72 | 68 | 64 | 61 | 57 | 54 | 50 | 47 | 44 | 40 | 37 | 34 | 31 | 28 | 25 | 22 | 19 | 17 | 14 | 11 | 8 | 6 | | | |
| 23° | 96 | 92 | 88 | 84 | 80 | 76 | 72 | 69 | 65 | 62 | 58 | 55 | 52 | 48 | 45 | 42 | 39 | 36 | 33 | 30 | 27 | 24 | 21 | 19 | 16 | 13 | 11 | 8 | 6 | | |
| 24° | 96 | 92 | 88 | 84 | 80 | 77 | 73 | 69 | 66 | 62 | 59 | 56 | 53 | 49 | 46 | 43 | 40 | 37 | 34 | 31 | 29 | 26 | 23 | 20 | 18 | 15 | 13 | 10 | 8 | 5 | |
| 25° | 96 | 92 | 88 | 84 | 81 | 77 | 74 | 70 | 67 | 63 | 60 | 57 | 54 | 50 | 47 | 44 | 41 | 39 | 36 | 33 | 30 | 28 | 25 | 22 | 20 | 17 | 15 | 12 | 10 | 8 | |
| 26° | 96 | 92 | 88 | 85 | 81 | 78 | 74 | 71 | 67 | 64 | 61 | 58 | 54 | 51 | 49 | 46 | 43 | 40 | 37 | 34 | 32 | 29 | 26 | 24 | 21 | 19 | 17 | 14 | 12 | 10 | |
| 27° | 96 | 92 | 89 | 85 | 82 | 78 | 75 | 71 | 68 | 65 | 62 | 58 | 56 | 52 | 50 | 47 | 44 | 41 | 38 | 36 | 33 | 31 | 28 | 26 | 23 | 21 | 18 | 16 | 14 | 12 | |
| 28° | 96 | 93 | 89 | 85 | 82 | 78 | 75 | 72 | 69 | 65 | 62 | 59 | 56 | 53 | 51 | 48 | 45 | 42 | 40 | 37 | 34 | 32 | 29 | 27 | 25 | 22 | 20 | 18 | 16 | 14 | 12 |
| 29° | 96 | 93 | 89 | 86 | 82 | 79 | 76 | 72 | 69 | 66 | 63 | 60 | 57 | 54 | 52 | 49 | 46 | 43 | 41 | 38 | 36 | 33 | 31 | 28 | 26 | 24 | 22 | 19 | 17 | 15 | 13 |
| 30° | 96 | 93 | 89 | 86 | 83 | 79 | 76 | 73 | 70 | 67 | 64 | 61 | 58 | 55 | 52 | 50 | 47 | 44 | 42 | 39 | 37 | 35 | 32 | 30 | 28 | 25 | 23 | 21 | 19 | 17 | 15 |

| Day | Temperature (°C) | | Temperature difference (°C) | Relative humidity (%) | Dew point temperature (°C) |
|---|---|---|---|---|---|
| | Dry | Wet | | | |
| 1 | | | | | |
| 2 | | | | | |
| 3 | | | | | |
| 4 | | | | | |
| 5 | | | | | |

## Summing Up

1. According to your text, what is relative humidity? _____
_____
_____

2. Define and describe a psychrometer. _____
_____
_____

3. According to your text, what is the definition of dew point? _____
_____
_____

4. Does the dew point increase or decrease as the relative humidity increases? _____
_____

5. What precipitation may appear at 0 °C if the relative humidity is high? _____
_____

Investigation

# 12J Measuring Precipitation

## Procedure

1. Tape a ruler to the side of the narrow glass jar so that the 0 cm mark is at the bottom. Measure the diameter of the jar.

   _____ cm

   The jar radius = $d/2$ = _____ cm.

2. Set the funnel in the top of the narrow jar. Measure the diameter of the funnel.

   _____

   The funnel radius = $d/2$ = _____ cm.

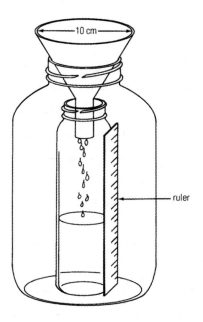

3. Place the narrow jar and funnel into the gallon jar.

4. Set the rain gauge on the roof, or anchor it to a stake in an open field.

5. Calculate how much actual rainfall 1 cm of accumulated water in the narrow jar would represent by using the following formula:

$$1 \text{ cm of water in the jar} = \frac{(\text{jar radius})^2}{(\text{funnel radius})^2} \text{ cm of actual rainfall}$$

6. Round to the nearest tenth of a centimeter.

## Observations

If the jar and funnel sizes listed at the beginning of this investigation are used, 10 cm of water in the inner jar equals 2.5 cm of rainfall.

1.  In the following table record the rainfall for three rainstorms.

| Date | Depth of water in jar (cm) | Rainfall (cm) | pH (optional) |
|------|----------------------------|---------------|---------------|
|      |                            |               |               |
|      |                            |               |               |
|      |                            |               |               |

(*Note*: If you have access to pH indicator paper or a pH meter, you might want to determine the pH of the rainwater from each storm.)

2.  Compare your answers to the local National Weather Service data for the same dates.

## Summing Up

1. Why should you place your rain gauge on the roof or in an open field? _____

_____

_____

2.  How would you measure the amount of rain if a rainstorm lasted for more than a day? _____

_____

_____

3.  How would you determine whether a certain depth of snow has as much water as the same depth of rain?

_____

_____

4.  Were there any dirt particles in the rainwater? If so, where did they come from? _____

_____

_____

Investigation
# 12K Weather Prediction Project

## Procedure

Observe the weather conditions for the next four days. Use your homemade weather instruments or commercially available instruments, or get the data from newspaper, radio, or television weather reports.

1. Record data on the weather table on page SA178.

2. Fill in the weather maps on page SA179, using the proper symbols. (Newspaper weather maps or maps from the Hydrometeorological Prediction Center web site will be helpful for this purpose.)

3. Using a red pen or pencil, sketch the jet stream on your weather map.

4. Fill in a station model on page SA180 using the data from page SA178 for each day. (See Applications 12D or Appendix A6 for a sample model.)

5. After you have recorded your data at the end of the third day, make predictions for the fourth day from all the data you have obtained. Record your predictions in the proper places on page SA178.

6. On the fourth day, record the actual data just as you did on the first three days.

### Goals
Record weather data for four consecutive days.

Complete a station model for each of the four days.

Predict the national and local weather for the fourth day.

### Materials
daily weather reports

pen or pencil

(optional) weather instruments (anemometer, barometer, thermometer, etc.)

## Summing Up

1. List any of your predictions that were far from the actual figures on the fourth day. _____
   _____
   _____
   _____

2. Why do you think your predictions were in error? _____
   _____
   _____
   _____

3. What additional information do you feel would have helped you make more accurate predictions?
   _____
   _____
   _____

4. From the weather information you collected, what effect does the jet stream appear to have on the weather?
   _____
   _____
   _____

| Condition | Day 1 | Day 2 | Day 3 | Day 4 Prediction | Day 4 Actual |
|---|---|---|---|---|---|
| Temperature | | | | | |
| Current weather | | | | | |
| Visibility | | | | | |
| Percent cloud cover | | | | | |
| Dew point | | | | | |
| Low cloud type | | | | | |
| Middle cloud type | | | | | |
| High cloud type | | | | | |
| Height of cloud base | | | | | |
| Amount of precipitation in last 6 hours | | | | | |
| Time precipitation began or ended | | | | | |
| Barometer reading a.m. | | | | | |
| Barometer reading p.m. | | | | | |
| Barometric change a.m. to p.m. | | | | | |
| Barometric tendency | | | | | |
| Wind speed | | | | | |
| Wind direction | | | | | |

**Day 1**

**Day 2**

**Day 3**

**Day 4**

Day 2

Day 1

Day 4

Day 3

SCIENCE

STUDENT ACTIVITIES

# 13 INTRODUCTION TO GEOLOGY

### Applications

## 13A What is Geology?

*Directions*: Answer the following questions in complete sentences.

1. What is the literal meaning of the word *geology*? _____
   _____

2. What is the definition of the word *geology*? _____
   _____
   _____

3. What is a geologist? _____
   _____
   _____

4. List five things that geologists might study. _____
   _____
   _____
   _____

5. How do geologists learn about the earth's interior? _____
   _____
   _____

Applications

# 13B The Earth's Interior

*Directions*: The figure shows a section of the earth's interior. Refer to the diagram as you complete the following questions.

1. Identify the parts labeled with numbers 1–8 on the drawing.

   1. _____     5. _____

   2. _____     6. _____

   3. _____     7. _____

   4. _____     8. _____

2. Describe the characteristics of regions 1, 4, and 8.

   Region 1 _____

   Region 4 _____

   _____

   Region 8 _____

3. Describe item 2, and tell how it was discovered. _____
   _____
   _____

4. What does *discontinuity* mean? _____
   _____

5. What percentage of the earth's volume are items 1, 5, and 6 respectively?

   Region 1 _____     Region 5 _____     Region 6 _____

6. Give the specified dimensions for each of the regions in the figure.

   Region 1   Thickness: _____

   Region 3   Depth: _____

   Region 4   Thickness: _____

   Region 5   Thickness: _____

   Region 6   Radius: _____

   Region 7   Thickness: _____

   Region 8   Radius: _____

Applications
# 13C The Structure of the Earth

*Directions*: Using the following words, label this diagram of the cross section of the earth. Then use the same words to answer the questions that follow.

crust   Moho   lithosphere   mantle   asthenosphere   core

_____ 1. The pressure and temperature of this part of the earth are extremely high.

_____ 2. This part of the earth is named after the Croatian scientist who discovered it.

_____ 3. This occupies about 84% of the earth's volume.

_____ 4. This part of the earth is solid, relatively low-density rock.

_____ 5. At some levels of this region, rock is thought to flow in slow convective patterns.

_____ 6. Two different zones of rock act together as a unit to form the plates of the earth's shell.

_____ 7. This marks the depth where earthquake waves suddenly change speed as they travel through the earth.

_____ 8. Most geologists believe this region consists of mostly iron, with some nickel, oxygen and several other light elements.

_____ 9. This is believed to have a liquid outer part.

_____ 10. All earthquake waves travel faster through this region than through the crust.

_____ 11. This region is an average of six times thicker under the continents than it is under the oceans.

_____ 12. This is a seismic discontinuity in the earth.

_____ 13. This region contains about 16% of the earth's volume.

_____ 14. Earthquake waves do not increase with depth as fast in this zone as they do in the rest of the mantle, perhaps because rocks are closer to melting at this depth.

_____ 15. Its thickness ranges from 7 km (4.5 mi) to 50 km (31 mi).

_____ 16. This occupies the earth's remaining volume below the mantle.

Applications

# 13D The Earth's History According to Creationists

*Directions*: Complete the sentences below with information consistent with a Creationist view of the earth's history.

1.  A person will not have a true appreciation for the world in which he lives until he is willing to face

    _____

    _____

2.  A Christian who studies the earth's history must remember these major events: _____

    _____

3.  God told us how _____ Creation took and how _____ it was.

    The _____ was a commemoration of the completed Creation.

4.  God cursed the earth because man _____.

5.  Though we do not know everything that happened as a result of the Curse, we know that there

    were many profound_____ in the earth and living things.

6.  God judged the earth at the time of the worldwide _____ of Noah's time
    by making permanent changes to it. Some examples of those changes include the following:

    _____

    _____

    _____

7.  People who deny the major events in Question 2 are said in 2 Peter 3:5–6 to be willingly _____.

8.  The Bible says that God created a fully functional world. Here are several examples
    of this fact:

    _____

    _____

    _____

    _____

    _____

9.  Imagine how a small part of the original creation looked. What would the land-
    forms have looked like? Try to picture in your mind all of the different kinds of
    organisms that might have inhabited this part of the earth. Write your description
    here:

    _____

    _____

    _____

    _____

    _____

10. God shows His _____ with wonders such as His physical creation.

Applications

# 13E Uniformitarianism

*Directions*: Complete the sentences below with information about uniformitarianism from pages 349–51.

1. Evolutionists try to learn about the earth's past by using the doctrine of _____, or uniformitarianism.

2. This doctrine says that the _____ is the key to the past.

3. People who accept uniformitarianism think that the processes occurring on the earth today are the same processes that have

   _____

4. To a certain extent, it is true that some aspects of nature do not change. For example, _____

   _____

5. Evolutionary scientists are in error when they believe that these scientific laws existed _____

   _____

6. Some evolutionists may believe in God; but if so, they believe that God is bound by _____

   _____

7. If uniformitarianism is correct, features unlike those forming today should not have formed in the past. Some examples of the earth's features seen today that are not observed to be forming today include the following:

   _____

8. Evolutionists believe that the ocean's water came from _____

9. The Bible warns against errors such as uniformitarianism in the following passage: _____

10. God has intervened _____ in the affairs of the world in the past and will do so again, contrary to what those who accept uniformitarianism may believe.

Applications

# 13F  Dating the Earth

*Directions*: In the spaces provided, write *True* if a statement is true and *False* if a statement is false.

_____ 1. Evolutionists and Creationists do not agree on the age of the earth.

_____ 2. Present-day observations can be used as a basis for determining the age of the earth.

_____ 3. Trying to find the earth's age from present processes is like trying to figure out how long a candle has been burning.

_____ 4. We can tell how old the earth is by looking at how fast various substances are accumulating and knowing how much of each substance is now present.

_____ 5. Evolutionists and Creationists agree on the earth's origin.

_____ 6. Many evolutionists believe that the earth began as a molten mass of rock that condensed out of a disk of dust.

_____ 7. Historical records can be used to help establish dates.

_____ 8. James Ussher calculated an age for the earth by referring to the genealogies given in Scripture.

_____ 9. An age of the earth obtained using biblical genealogical records is completely certain because the records are found in Scripture.

_____ 10. A process that is known to occur at a constant rate, such as radioactive decay, may be used to determine the age of an object if all other assumptions that a researcher makes are scientifically reasonable.

Applications

# 13G  Three Methods of Dating the Earth

*Directions*: Read the following statements carefully and decide which of the types of dating method are being described. Then indicate your answers by writing the proper letters in the blanks provided. Some statements have more than one answer.

_____ 1. A worthwhile tool if used with the proper precautions

_____ 2. Does not involve carbon in any form

_____ 3. Gave ages ranging from 160 million years to 3 billion years for volcanic rocks known to be only 170 years old

_____ 4. Unreliable for ages beyond about 5000 years

_____ 5. Based on the assumption that the ratio of one substance to another indicates the age

_____ 6. Used only on materials containing carbon

_____ 7. Uses a calibration curve to determine ages

_____ 8. Makes an unscientific assumption about the contents of the original rock

_____ 9. May use a liquid scintillation counter

_____ 10. Based on the fact that radioactive elements are unstable and break down into other elements or isotopes

> a. Radiocarbon dating
> b. Uranium-lead method
> c. Potassium-argon method

Investigation
# 13H The Radiocarbon Method

If you obtain a number of carbon-containing samples of known age and measure their radioactivity per unit weight, you can construct a graph of radioactivity versus age. This is called a *calibration curve*. Once you have such a graph, you can then find the age of an unknown sample by a simple two-step procedure. First, measure its radioactivity per unit weight with a counter. Second, read its age from the graph.

This method of dating, called the radiocarbon method, does have some problems. One difficulty is that the calibration curve cuts off at about 5000 years. Therefore, the oldest samples that this method can legitimately handle will be about 5000 years old. Another difficulty is that the amount of carbon-14 in the atmosphere has not stayed the same down through the centuries. In spite of these difficulties, radiocarbon dates (if restricted to the last 5000 years) are reasonably accurate. For this reason the method appears to have definite merit and will undoubtedly continue to be used by scientists.

## Procedures and observations

1. Construct a calibration curve.

   a. Plot the following information on the graph given below. (*Note*: The vertical axis represents the radioactivity [disintegration per gram per minute—abbreviated d/g/m] of the sample as

## Goals
Construct a calibration curve, using data from objects of known age. Use the calibration curve to date several objects of unknown age.

## Materials
ruler

measured with a radiation detector. The horizontal axis represents the age of the sample as measured by an independent dating method [something other than radiocarbon], such as a human historical record.)

   b. Draw the best smooth curve you can through the points. It should intersect most of the points without sharp breaks or bends. Sketch the curve lightly at first; then darken it as you become more sure of its location.

### DATA FOR CALIBRATION CURVE

| Material | Known age (y) | Radioactivity (d/g/m) |
|---|---|---|
| 1. Tree ring | 880 | 13.7 |
| 2. Tree ring | 1370 | 13.3 |
| 3. Tree ring | 1375 | 12.8 |
| 4. Manuscript | 2050 | 12.0 |
| 5. Mummy (Ptolemy) | 2150 | 11.6 |
| 6. Mummy (Tayinat) | 2625 | 11.2 |
| 7. Redwood tree | 2930 | 11.0 |
| 8. Mummy (Sesostris) | 3870 | 9.8 |
| 9. Mummy (Sneferu) | 4575 | 8.4 |
| 10. Mummy (Zoser) | 4750 | 8.3 |
| 11. Mummy (Hemaka) | 5000 | 7.2 |

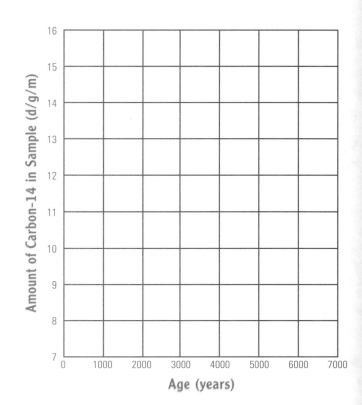

2. Use the calibration curve to date the following four samples.

| Material | Radioactivity (d/g/m) | Age (y) |
|---|---|---|
| 1.  Bone | 12.4 | |
| 2.  Wood | 8.8 | |
| 3.  Charcoal | 10.7 | |
| 4.  Linen | 11.5 | |

  a. Locate the amount of carbon-14 in the sample on the vertical axis.

  b. Draw a line from this point to the calibration curve. Then draw a line from the curve down to the horizontal axis. Read the age from the horizontal axis and record it in the chart.

## Summing Up

1. Suppose that another method indicated the age of the piece of bone in Step 2 to be 500 years.

   Does this agree with the age you gave the piece of bone? _____

   If the ages do not agree, what term would you use to refer to this sample? _____

2. Suppose someone gave you a sample whose radioactivity measured 7.0 d/g/m.

   Could you use the calibration curve you made to estimate its age? _____

   Why or why not? _____

   _____

3. To what specific kinds of materials is the radiocarbon method applicable? _____

   _____

   _____

4. Does the radiocarbon method in any way help to establish that the earth is millions

   or billions of years old? _____ Explain. _____

   _____

   _____

5. Compared to a fossil, does a living organism have a large or a small amount of radioactivity?

   _____

# 14 MINERALS AND ORES

Applications

## 14A Types of Matter

### PART 1: ORGANIC AND INORGANIC

*Directions*: According to your text, minerals by definition do not contain carbon (or any other elements or compounds of organic origin). Classify the following substances under the heading "Organic Materials" or "Inorganic Materials."

| | | | |
|---|---|---|---|
| coal | igneous rocks | shells | silver |
| fingernails | iron | copper | wood |
| gold | oil | hair | platinum |

**Organic Materials**                    **Inorganic Materials**

_____        _____

_____        _____

_____        _____

_____        _____

_____        _____

### PART 2: DEFINITIONS AND DESCRIPTIONS

_____ 1.  Anything that has mass and occupies space

_____ 2.  Substances that are made up of either one element or one compound

_____ 3.  Materials that are made up of two or more pure substances not chemically combined; the materials do not have a fixed ratio of elements and can be separated into their substances by physical means

_____ 4.  Pure substances made up of only one kind of atom

_____ 5.  Pure substances made up of two or more kinds of atoms chemically combined; they have a fixed ratio of elements

_____ 6.  Substances that are mostly carbon compounds (or other materials) that are products of living things

_____ 7.  Substances that do not contain substantial amounts of carbon or do not come from living things

_____ 8.  List two more organic substances other than those listed above.

_____

Applications

# 14B Mineral Tests

*Directions*: Read the following descriptions carefully and decide which type of mineral identification property or test is being described. Write the correct letters in the blanks provided.

_____ 1. Has five ratings: perfect, good, fair, poor, and none

_____ 2. Is specific for each mineral because it is based on the arrangement of atoms in the mineral

_____ 3. Sometimes changes when exposed to air

_____ 4. Is always the same in spite of impurities

_____ 5. Is measured using the Mohs scale, which ranges from 1 to 10

_____ 6. Deals with the number of directions or planes in which a mineral will break

_____ 7. Describes the way light reflects from a mineral's surface

_____ 8. Testing can involve the use of these common objects: fingernail, penny, glass plate, knife blade, and steel file

_____ 9. Uses a platinum wire dipped into a powder of the mineral

_____ 10. Is performed to see if the mineral will give off gas (effervescence)

_____ 11. Is identified and measured using a radiation detector

_____ 12. A measure of the amount that light is bent or rotated as it passes through a mineral

_____ 13. The characteristic color that is produced when a mineral is rubbed across the surface of unglazed porcelain

_____ 14. Descriptions include vitreous, pearly, adamantine, earthy, greasy, dull, and resinous

_____ 15. The tendency to break into flat sheets or along certain planes

_____ 16. The ability to withstand scratching and abrasion

_____ 17. A property of lodestone

_____ 18. Produces a double image as light passes through certain minerals

_____ 19. Involves the absorption of invisible ultraviolet light and the production of a glow or afterglow

_____ 20. Is estimated by lifting

_____ 21. Is more reliable than outward color

_____ 22. Involves enlargement by accretion

_____ 23. Is the ratio of the weight of a mineral to the weight of an equal volume of water

_____ 24. Involves fluorescence or phosphorescence

a. Color
b. Streak
c. Luster
d. Crystal shape
e. Cleavage
f. Hardness
g. Specific gravity
h. Flame test
i. Acid test
j. Magnetism
k. Radioactivity
l. Luminescence
m. Refraction or Polarization

Applications
# 14C Elements and Compounds

*Directions*: In Part 1 write the names of the minerals under the heading "Elements" or "Compounds." In Part 2 read each statement carefully and then decide which mineral is being described. Write the correct mineral names in the blanks provided. Two of the statements have two correct answers. Two of the minerals are not used.

| | | | | |
|---|---|---|---|---|
| bauxite | copper | galena | platinum | silver |
| calcite | diamond | gold | quartz | sulfur |

## PART 1

### Elements

_____

_____

_____

_____

_____

_____

### Compounds

_____

_____

_____

_____

_____

_____

## PART 2

1. Mined with dredges _____

2. Sticks to grease during separation from ore _____

3. Burns with a blue flame _____

4. Used by the Native Americans _____

5. Almost always mixed with silver _____

6. First discovered in Colombia, South America _____

7. Obtained mainly as a byproduct of the fossil fuel industries _____

8. Composed of a metal and sulfur _____

9. Usually pale yellow or colorless _____

10. Has perfect cleavage _____

11. Has a metallic luster (five items) _____

12. Found in Louisiana and Texas _____

13. Weighed in units called carats _____

14. Mined extensively from placer deposits _____

15. Sometimes retrieved by panning _____

16. Is yellow with conchoidal fracture _____

(continued on next page)

| bauxite | copper | galena | platinum | silver |
|---------|---------|--------|----------|--------|
| calcite | diamond | gold | quartz | sulfur |

17. Has a greasy luster when uncut _____

18. Found near active or extinct volcanoes and in sedimentary beds deep underground _____

19. Has the chemical name silicon dioxide _____

20. Mined from the Argyle pipe in Australia _____

21. The second most abundant mineral in the earth's crust _____

22. Found in fine strands, thin sheets, and irregular masses _____

23. Mined today in Russia and South Africa _____

24. Found on the Keweenaw Peninsula, Michigan _____

25. Produces a silver-white streak _____

Investigation
# 14D Accretion of Crystals

Minerals form various crystal structures in nature. In this investigation you will be able to observe crystal formation that is similar to mineral crystal formation. You will grow crystals from solutions of sugar, alum, and Epsom salts. Though sugar is not a mineral, it does form crystals.

## Procedure

1. Add 100 mL of water to the saucepan and bring it to a boil. Remove the saucepan from the hot plate.

2. Slowly stir the sugar into the hot water. Continue to add sugar until no more will dissolve.

3. Add enough food coloring to color the solution. (optional)

4. Pour the solution into a *clean* glass beaker. Do not include any of the undissolved sugar.

5. Tie one end of a string around the rod or pencil. Lay the rod across the beaker, with the other end of the string dangling down into the sugar solution. Adjust the string until the end is at least a centimeter above the bottom of the beaker.

6. Put the beaker in a place where it will be undisturbed for several days. Avoid direct sunlight or heating system ducts.

## Goal
Grow crystals and compare the crystal shapes of various substances.

## Materials
saucepan
water
hot plate or stove
sugar (sucrose), 200 g
alum (aluminum ammonium sulfate), 100 g
Epsom salts (magnesium sulfate heptahydrate), 100 g
food coloring (optional)
glass beakers, 250 mL (3)
rods, glass or metal, or pencils (3)
cotton strings, 15 cm (3)
hand magnifying lens

7. Repeat Steps 1–6 with the alum and with the Epsom salts.

8. After several days remove each string and allow the crystals to dry. Observe the crystals with a magnifying lens. Draw the shape of each type of crystal in the space below.

| Sugar | Alum | Epsom Salts |
|---|---|---|
|  |  |  |

## Summing Up

1. As each solution cools, it is said to be *supersaturated*. What do you think this means? _____
   _____    _____
   _____

2. Why do you think the solution is supersaturated when cool but not supersaturated when hot? _____
   _____
   _____

3. What formed on the string? _____
   _____

4. Are the crystals that you observed separate crystals? _____
   _____

5. When you stir sugar into a drink such as tea, it disappears. What happens to it? _____
   _____
   _____

6. How could you recrystallize the sugar stirred into a cup of tea? _____
   _____
   _____

Investigation

# 14E Accretion of Crystals—Going a Step Further

## Procedure

1. Put 200 mL of water into the saucepan and bring it to a boil. Remove the saucepan from the hot plate.

2. Stir in as much solute as can be dissolved.

3. Pour the solution equally into two Styrofoam cups. Do not include any of the undissolved solute.

4. Tie one end of a string around a rod or pencil. Lay the rod across one of the cups, with the other end of the string dangling down into the solution.

5. Place the other cup of solution inside the remaining empty cup to insulate the solution. Punch a small hole near the center of the small Styrofoam plate. Tie one end of a string around a pencil or rod, and push the other end of the string through the hole in the plate. Cover the doubled cups with the small Styrofoam plate, allowing the string to dangle into the solution.

6. Place the doubled cups where they will not be disturbed.

7. Set the single cup in a refrigerator.

8. Observe from time to time over several hours. Allow the solutions to stand undisturbed overnight.

9. Observe the crystals with a magnifying glass.

### Goal
Determine the effect of temperature on crystal formation.

### Materials
water, 200 mL

saucepan

hot plate or stove

twice as much of the solute in Investigation 14D that you think made the best crystals

Styrofoam cups (3)

cotton strings, 15 cm (2)

rods, glass or metal, or pencils (2)

small Styrofoam plate

refrigerator

## Summing Up

1. In which cup were the larger crystals formed? _____
_____

2. What caused some crystals to be larger? _____
_____
_____

3. What does this experiment tell you about the size of crystals found in various minerals? _____
_____
_____

4. How could you grow even larger crystals? _____
_____
_____
_____

Investigation

# 14F  Properties of Minerals

Minerals are naturally occurring, inorganic, crystalline solids that form the building blocks of rocks. Though well over three thousand minerals are known, only a few make up the bulk of the rocks in the earth's crust. This investigation will deal with a representative sampling of those common rock-forming minerals.

## Procedure

Five different identifying properties will be covered in Part 1 of this study: color, streak, luster, hardness, and specific gravity. Several other properties will be briefly noted in Part 2.

## PART 1

1. *Color.* "Color" refers to the appearance of the mineral in ordinary light. Record the color of the following minerals.

    bauxite (ore) _____

    magnetite _____

    chalcopyrite _____

    microcline _____

    galena _____

    milky quartz _____

    gypsum _____

    pyrite _____

    hematite _____

    rose quartz _____

2. *Streak.* "Streak" is the color of the powdered mineral. If the hardness of the specimen is less than 7, you can perform the streak test by rubbing the specimen against unglazed porcelain and observing the color of the mark it produces. Perform the streak test on each of the following (all of which are relatively soft minerals) and record the color in each case.

    magnetite _____

    chalcopyrite _____

    galena _____

    gypsum _____

    hematite _____

    calcite _____

## Goal

Study some of the more readily observed properties used to identify minerals.

## Materials

rock and mineral collection

ceramic tile or streak plate

copper penny (pre-1983)

steel knife

glass plate

beaker, 250 mL–1 L

thread

ring stand

spring balance or mass balance

hand magnifying lens

magnet

3. *Luster.* "Luster" is a rating of how a mineral reflects light. If a mineral has a shiny silver or gold appearance like a metal, it is said to have a metallic luster. If it is shiny like glass, it is said to have a vitreous luster. If it is not shiny (if it is like chalk, for example), it is said to have a dull luster. Record the luster of each of the following minerals.

    bauxite _____

    chalcopyrite _____

    calcite _____

    galena _____

4. *Hardness.* In this test common objects are used to test the hardness of mineral specimens: a fingernail (hardness of 2.5), a copper penny (hardness of 3.5), a steel knife blade (hardness of 5.0–5.5), and a glass plate (hardness of 5.5). Hardness is estimated as follows:

### Mohs Hardness Number

1  can easily be scratched with the fingernail

2  can barely be scratched with the fingernail

3  cannot be scratched with the fingernail but can be scratched with a penny

4  cannot be scratched with a penny but can be scratched easily with a steel knife blade

5  can barely be scratched with a steel knife blade

6  cannot be scratched with a steel knife blade but is hard enough to scratch glass

7+  can easily scratch a steel knife blade and glass

When testing whether a mineral will scratch the glass plate, do not hold the glass plate in your hands; keep it firmly flat on the table or desktop. Also, if you think you have scratched the glass, wet your index finger and see whether you can rub off the scratch mark. If it comes off, it was merely some of the mineral that rubbed off onto the glass. A true scratch mark will remain.

(*Note*: It is not necessary to scratch back and forth several times to determine hardness. A single stroke is sufficient.)

Determine as nearly as you can the hardness of each of the following:

calcite _____     gypsum _____

corundum _____     magnetite _____

fluorite _____     muscovite _____

galena _____     quartz _____

5. *Specific Gravity.* To measure specific gravity, a thread is tied to the specimen and it is hung from a spring balance or triple beam balance. The specimen is weighed first when it is in the air and again when it is completely submerged (but not resting on the bottom) in a beaker of water. The mineral weighs less when submerged because of the buoyant force of the water. The difference in weight is equal to the weight of the displaced water. The weight of the mineral in air divided by the difference in weight when weighed under water gives the specific gravity of the mineral.

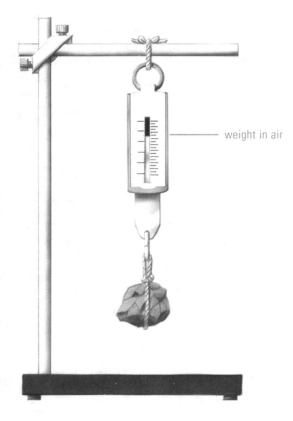

weight in air

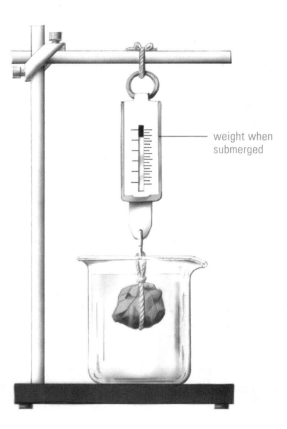

weight when submerged

6. Determine the specific gravity of the following minerals. Before weighing them, estimate their density by "hefting" one in the palm of each hand. You can readily determine that there is a difference in their specific gravities. Record your measurements and calculations below.

<table>
<tr><td style="text-align:center">Calcite</td><td style="text-align:center">Magnetite</td></tr>
</table>

Weight in air _____

Weight in air _____

Weight submerged _____

Weight submerged _____

Difference _____

Difference _____

$$s.g. = \frac{\text{weight (mass) in air}}{\text{weight (mass) difference}}$$

Specific gravity _____

Specific gravity _____

# PART 2

1. Study the angles of your calcite crystal sample. Use a hand lens to examine the surface closely. Note that there are many little parallelograms. Calcite has a characteristic rhombohedral crystal shape. The acute plane angles that you see between the face surfaces are about 75°; the obtuse angles, 105°.

2. Some minerals have a characteristic feel. Note the greasy feel of your talc sample.

3. Note that both muscovite and biotite (mica) consist of innumerable thin sheets. This gives them one-direction cleavage (also called basal cleavage). Do not flake sheets off your mica samples unless told to do so.

4. Observe whether your magnetite sample can be picked up with a magnet. Are any other minerals in the collection magnetic?

## Summing Up

1. Why is the identification of unknown minerals possible and, in some cases, very easy? _____

2. Are all the minerals in your collection naturally occurring, or are some of them manmade? _____

3. All of the streak tests you performed were for relatively soft materials. How would you perform a streak test for a mineral whose hardness is 8.5?

4. What is the relationship of minerals to rocks? _____

5. Some of the minerals in the collection are called ores; others are not. What is the difference between them?

# 15 ROCKS AND FOSSILS

## 15A Classification of Rocks

*Directions*: Arrange the following items in an outline in the space provided. (*Hint*: There are two subpoints under each main point.) Then write a definition for each main point and each subpoint. Finally, circle the names of the three rocks that are the most common fossil-bearing rocks.

| | | | |
|---|---|---|---|
| anthracite (hard coal) | foliated metamorphic rocks | lignite (brown coal) | pumice |
| basalt | gabbro | limestone | quartzite |
| bituminous coal (soft coal) | gneiss | marble | sandstone |
| clastic (fragmental) | granite | metamorphic rocks | schist |
|   sedimentary rocks | granite gneiss | nonclastic (chemical) | scoria |
| conglomerate | halite |   sedimentary rocks | sedimentary rocks |
| diorite gneiss | hornblende gneiss | nonfoliated metamorphic | siltstone and shale |
| extrusive igneous rocks | igneous rocks |   rocks | slate |
| felsite | intrusive igneous rocks | obsidian | |

I. _____

II. _____

III. _____

Applications

# 15B Fossils

*Directions*: Use the material on fossils, pages 391–400, to answer the following questions.

1. What is a fossil? _____
   _____

2. What do fossils reveal? _____
   _____

3. What do fossils *not* support? _____
   _____

4. Why are "missing link" fossils a powerful evidence for Creation and not for evolution? _____
   _____
   _____

5. How do dinosaur fossils give evidence for a worldwide flood? _____
   _____
   _____

6. What are the three categories that all of the fossils that supposedly prove man's animal ancestry fall into?
   _____
   _____

7. How is a trilobite fossil and the age of the rock in which it is found an example of how evolutionists use circular reasoning?
   _____
   _____
   _____

8. What is a polystrate fossil? _____
   _____

9. How do polystrate fossils provide evidence for rapid burial in the Flood? _____
   _____
   _____
   _____

10. How do evolutionists believe coal formed? _____
    _____
    _____

11. Through experimentation, how quickly have scientists found that coal can form if the temperature and pressure are correct?
    _____

12. What are some evidences that coal formed quickly instead of over many years? _____
    _____
    _____

Applications
# 15C Characteristics of Rocks

*Directions*: Select the proper terms from the list to complete the statements below. Write your answers on the blanks provided. You may use each term only once, but more than one term may be used to complete a statement.

| | | | |
|---|---|---|---|
| basalt | foliated | laccolith | regional metamorphism |
| breccia | fossil-bearing | magma | remains |
| clastic | fossils | matrix | rock |
| coal | fuel | metamorphic | rock cycle |
| conglomerate | gas | natural | salt |
| dikes | gneiss | nonclastic | schist |
| domes | igneous | plant | sedimentary |
| extrusive | index | polystrate | sill |
| felsic | intrusive | porphyry | strata |

1. The coarsest grade of clastic sedimentary rock is called _____.

2. Any traces of a living organism preserved by natural means are called _____.

3. _____ is a conglomerate rock containing sharp and angular fragments.

4. A coarsely foliated rock with a banded appearance is called _____.

5. The solid form of fossil fuel is _____.

6. Changes to rocks over wide areas is called _____.

7. _____ igneous rocks form above the earth's surface.

8. Rocks that cool from a molten mixture are called _____.

9. _____ are layers of sedimentary rock.

10. Molten rock beneath the earth's surface is called _____.

11. Both Creationists and evolutionists believe coal formed from _____.

12. A common metamorphic rock that splits easily is called _____.

13. Evolutionists attempt to use fossils called _____ fossils to determine the age of rock strata.

14. A _____ is a small dome-like plutonic intrusion that often forms rounded hills on the earth's surface.

15. Rock containing two very different sizes of crystals is called _____.

16. _____ igneous rocks formed beneath the earth's crust.

17. Igneous rocks that contain much silica are classified as _____ rocks.

18. Fossil _____ comes in solid, liquid, and gaseous forms.

19. _____ fossils extend through several layers of sedimentary rock that supposedly represent long periods of time.

20. Limestone, sandstone, and shale are the most common examples of _____ rocks.

21. _____ are formed by magma that fills cracks that cut across existing rock layers.

22. The gaseous form of fossil fuel is _____.

(continued on next page)

| basalt | foliated | laccolith | regional metamorphism |
| breccia | fossil-bearing | magma | remains |
| clastic | fossils | matrix | rock |
| coal | fuel | metamorphic | rock cycle |
| conglomerate | gas | natural | salt |
| dikes | gneiss | nonclastic | schist |
| domes | igneous | plant | sedimentary |
| extrusive | index | polystrate | sill |
| felsic | intrusive | porphyry | strata |

23. A _____ is a material in which something is embedded.

24. _____ sedimentary rock forms from pieces eroded from other rock.

25. Rocks that are made of particles bonded together by natural cements are called _____ rocks.

26. Halite occasionally exists in nature as vertical cylindrical masses called _____.

27. A former sedimentary or igneous rock altered by heat or pressure is called a _____ rock.

28. _____ is a dark, greenish gray, extrusive igneous rock.

29. _____ sedimentary rocks form from minerals dissolved in water.

30. _____ rocks have bands or layers.

31. A _____ is a sheet of igneous rock that forced its way between layers of existing rock.

32. A _____ consists of one or more minerals.

33. The progression from magma, to igneous rock, through erosion to a sedimentary rock, and back to magma, is one possible path of what geologists call the _____.

Investigation
# 15D Properties of Rocks

Rocks are the materials of which the earth's crust is made. Now that you have studied some of the important rock-building minerals, you should understand the make-up of rocks more fully than you did before. In this exercise you will be examining about two dozen rock specimens made up of an approximately equal number from each of the three major categories—igneous, sedimentary, and metamorphic.

## Procedure

### Igneous Rocks

Study the specimens of igneous rocks in your collection.

1. List the igneous rocks that are lightest colored. These rocks have a high silica content.

   _____

2. List the ones that are dark colored (black or dark gray). These rocks have a low silica content.

   _____

3. Which two specimens are coarse grained? These are intrusive igneous rocks that cooled under conditions that permitted the formation of large visible crystals.

   _____

4. Which of these two has a porphyritic texture (some large grains in a matrix of smaller crystals)? This rock may have cooled in two different stages.

   _____

5. Granite is made up of three minerals that can be identified by their colors. Name the following three minerals:

   pink or tan _____

   black _____

   white _____

6. Which specimens have a porous structure? These are volcanic rocks that have bubble holes due to trapped gases.

   _____

7. Test your pumice specimen to see if it floats on water. There is a good chance that its overall density will be less than that of water. Does it float?

   _____

## Goal
Examine the properties of representative samples from the three major classes of rocks.

## Materials
rock and mineral collection (50 specimens)
hand magnifying lens or stereo microscope
beaker, 250 mL–1 L
eyedropper
hydrochloric acid, dilute (2 *M*)

8. Which rock exhibits the best example of conchoidal fracture? This rock was formed from magma or lava that had no dissolved gases and cooled relatively quickly at low pressures.

   _____

### Sedimentary Rocks

Study the specimens of sedimentary rocks in your collection.

1. Which of the samples shows the best evidence of layering (stratification)?

   _____

2. Dip each of the seven specimens into a beaker of water, and note which one exhibits an earthy smell.

   _____

3. Dry your specimens with a paper towel. Place them in a row on a clean paper towel. Place a single drop of dilute hydrochloric acid on each one with an eyedropper. Which ones effervesce (fizz)?

   _____

   Rinse the acid from each specimen under a faucet after you have finished testing it.

4. Examine your conglomerate rock specimen.

   What color is the matrix? _____

   Note the wide range in the sizes of the fragments. Are the fragments interlocking or separate?

   _____

5. Which of the sedimentary rocks is porous? _____

_____

6. Which type of rock is regarded as a potentially useful source of fossil fuel?

_____

## Metamorphic Rocks

Study the specimens of metamorphic rocks in your collection.

1. From what rock was gneiss probably formed? _____

   slate? _____ quartzite? _____

   marble? _____ anthracite? _____

2. Which of your specimens exhibit foliation? _____

_____

3. Dip each of the eight specimens into a beaker of water, and note which one exhibits an earthy smell.

   _____

4. Dry your specimens with a paper towel. Add a drop of dilute hydrochloric acid to each one with a medicine dropper. Which one effervesces?

   _____

   Rinse the acid from each specimen under a faucet after you have finished testing it.

## Summing Up

1. Name one property that could be useful in identifying both rocks and minerals.

_____

_____

Properties that are not valid for both include streak, hardness, gross cleavage, and luster.

2. Which of the three major classes of rocks exhibits true stratification?

_____

3. What evidence did you find that slate is related to shale? _____

Foliation is not stratification, although it can be easily mistaken for it.

_____

4. What evidence did you find that marble is chemically similar to limestone?

_____

5. Which of your metamorphic rocks did you observe to be nonfoliated?

_____

Investigation

# 15E Fallacies of the Geologic Time Scale

Since you know that the concept of evolution is erroneous, you should reject all schemes of thought that are built upon it. The *geologic time scale* is one such scheme. It is a speculative framework of the earth's history. If evolution had happened, it would have had to have happened slowly and continuously. However, geologists have noticed that new fossil organisms seem to appear in the geologic column fully formed in stages. Each of these stages is given a name and assigned a period of time on the geologic time scale. The largest units of these time periods are called *eras*, the next smaller, *periods*, and the next, *epochs*. Evolutionists claim that these time units can be related to the appearance and extinction of fossil organisms in the earth's rock layers.

An evolutionary geologist believes that representative plants and animals living in each age were buried in sediment by rivers or streams, local floods, dust storms, mudslides, or wave action. In time this sediment turned to rock. The process is said to have been repeated many times, producing layer upon layer of rock, with each new layer representing a time period more recent than the one beneath it (the principle of *superposition*). The evolutionary geologist believes he can tell how old a fossil is by its vertical location with respect to other fossils. But his dating method is full of circular reasoning. He dates rocks by the fossils found in them and dates fossils by the same rocks. In addition, the method is flawed by the basic assumption of evolution. Living things were rapidly created; they did not slowly evolve. Further, there is good reason to believe that most of the fossils were laid down in a year-long period of great catastrophic activity during the Genesis Flood, not over hundreds of millions of years of more gentle activity, as is generally claimed.

## Procedure

1. In each column of the table on page SA210, draw a vertical line through the portion of the geologic time scale affected by each numbered item described below. (*Note*: Look at the first column, and then plot the other seven items in the same manner.)

2. Place arrowheads at the ends of the line and make short horizontal lines at the arrowheads to mark the limits of the periods.

3. On each vertical line, place a label describing the evidence. For example, the label for Column 1 is "Iron Pot in Coal."

*Column 1.* An iron pot was found embedded in coal. The coal was determined to be middle Pennsylvanian, so one end of the line is placed in the middle of the Pennsyl-

vanian period. The iron pot must actually have been made in very recent times; so the other end of the line is located on the dashed line near the top of the table.

*Column 2.* Gymnosperm pollen is found in the Grand Canyon in the lowest strata (Precambrian). Yet evolutionists claim that such plants did not evolve until the Permian. Draw your line from the top of the Precambrian to the middle of the Permian. Label the line "Pollen in Grand Canyon."

*Column 3.* Fossil wood was found embedded in Precambrian rock in northern Quebec, Canada. Two radiocarbon tests on samples of the wood gave results of about four thousand years. Assuming that the radiocarbon results are correct, draw your line from the top of the Precambrian to the dashed line at the top of the table. Label it "Fossil Wood in Precambrian."

*Column 4.* A baked clay figurine 4 cm long was brought up from a depth of 92 m by a team of workers drilling for water at Nampa, Idaho. The level at which it was found was determined to be early Pliocene. Draw your line from the lowest part of the Pliocene to the dashed line at the top of the table. Label it "Nampa Image."

*Column 5.* Cambrian and Mississippian layers are found to alternate back and forth (two complete cycles) in one part of the north rim of the Grand Canyon. Since time cannot alternate back and forth, the portion of the geologic time table encompassed by the Cambrian and Mississippian periods is invalidated by this discovery. Draw your line from the middle of the Cambrian to the middle of the Mississippian and label it "Alternating Layers."

*Column 6.* Chief Mountain in Glacier National Park in Montana consists of Precambrian rock overlying Cretaceous rock. Since the fossils are out of their alleged developmental order, evolutionists have attempted to salvage their theory by claiming that an overthrust rearranged rock that was originally in its correct order. Yet

---

### Goal
Graph evidence that contradicts the geologic time scale, using three different lines of evidence—fossils, artifacts, and alleged geologic overthrusts.

### Materials
none

none of the evidences of overthrusting are present. The only logical conclusion is that the rocks were deposited in the order in which they are now found, meaning that the alleged time span between the Precambrian and Cretaceous (about 500 million years) never existed. Draw your line from the top of the Precambrian to the top of the Cretaceous and label it "Chief Mountain."

Columns 7 & 8. Your teacher may provide other examples.

| Eon | Era | Period | Epoch | Contradictions (1 2 3 4 5 6 7 8) | Millions of years before the present |
|---|---|---|---|---|---|
| Phanerozoic | | | | | |
| | Cenozoic | Quaternary | Recent (Holocene) | | 0.01 |
| | | | Pleistocene | | 1.6 |
| | | Tertiary | Pliocene | | 5.3 |
| | | | Miocene | | 23.7 |
| | | | Oligocene | | 35.6 |
| | | | Eocene | | 56.8 |
| | | | Paleocene | | 66.4 |
| | Mesozoic | Cretaceous | | Iron Pot in Coal | 144 |
| | | Jurassic | | | 208 |
| | | Triassic | | | 245 |
| | Paleozoic | Permian | | | 286 |
| | | Pennsylvanian | | | 320 |
| | | Mississippian | | | 365 |
| | | Devonian | | | 408 |
| | | Silurian | | | 438 |
| | | Ordovician | | | 520 |
| | | Cambrian | | | 555 |
| Precambrian | Proterozoic | | | | 2500 |
| | Archean | | | | 3800 |
| | Hadean | | | | 4600 |

## Observations

1. The vertical line drawn through a geologic time unit has the effect of canceling it. Look at the overall effect of the six contradictions. How much of the fossil-bearing geologic time scale survived?

_____

2. List the surviving parts of the table. _____

_____

## Summing Up

1. On what basis do evolutionists label rocks as "Cretaceous," "Cambrian," and so on? _____

_____

2. Explain how circular reasoning enters into the dating of rocks and fossils. _____

_____

_____

3. What three different kinds of evidence were examined in this exercise? _____

_____

_____

4. Assuming that a human artifact has been discovered embedded in sedimentary rock, and scientists agree that the artifact appears to be genuine, how could this fact be explained biblically?

_____

_____

Investigation
# 15F "Trilobite-ology"

A common and easily recognized kind of fossil is a trilobite. Trilobite bodies consisted of three lobes arranged side by side along their length, hence the name, *tri-lobite*. Trilobites are placed in the animal phylum Arthropoda, as are insects, spiders, shrimp, and crabs, because they had exoskeletons and jointed appendages. In fact, some trilobites looked very similar to young horseshoe crabs of today. However, there are no known living trilobites today; they are considered to be extinct. All that is known about trilobites has come from studying their fossils and making "educated guesses" by comparing them with living arthropods.

## Procedure and observations

### PART 1: THE TRILOBITE BODY

1. Study Diagram A. Notice the raised middle lobe that runs from the head through the tail. Two sections are on either side of the middle lobe and are separated from the middle lobe by the longitudinal (long-wise) *axial furrows*. Trilobites get their name from these three longitudinal lobes.

2. The body can also be divided into three lengthwise sections: *head* (or *cephalon*), *thorax*, and *tail* (or *pygidium*). Often only one of the sections will have been preserved in a fossil. This is because, like most marine arthropods, trilobites molted their exoskeleton as they grew. So many trilobite fossils are just portions of the shed exoskeleton.

3. Notice the eyes and variously-shaped sections of the cephalon. The size, shape, and position of these parts are useful in identification of different trilobite species.

4. How many smaller segments (*pleura*) are there in the thorax?

   _____

   Under each of these segments were gills attached to two pairs of legs for swimming or crawling. The number of segments in the thorax is also used to help identify different species of trilobites.

5. Observe that the pygidium is also made up of several sections. However, in the pygidium, the segments apparently grew together in the form of an inflexible plate.

6. Now study Diagram B. You should notice that although it is a trilobite, the size, shape, position, and number of the various parts are different from

### Goal
Study a trilobite fossil and identify its various structural parts. Identify the subgroup to which particular trilobites belong.

### Materials
hand lens or stereo microscope
trilobite fossil(s)

the one in Diagram A. Label Diagram B using the same terms that were used with Diagram A. Have your teacher check your work before you proceed further with this investigation.

7. Observe Diagrams C, D, E, and F. Note the scale with each one; some trilobites were up to 70 cm long, whereas others were less than 1 cm. While each differs in *morphology* (structure), they are all trilobites. The fossil record indicates that there were over ten thousand species of trilobites.

**Diagram A**

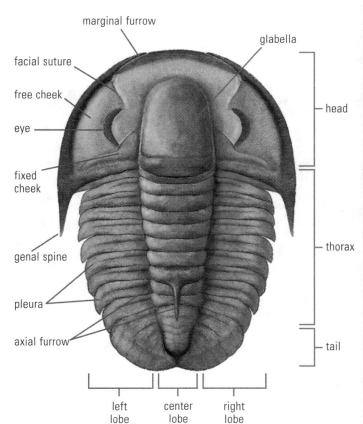

marginal furrow
glabella
facial suture
free cheek
eye
fixed cheek
genal spine
pleura
axial furrow
head
thorax
tail
left lobe
center lobe
right lobe

## Diagram B

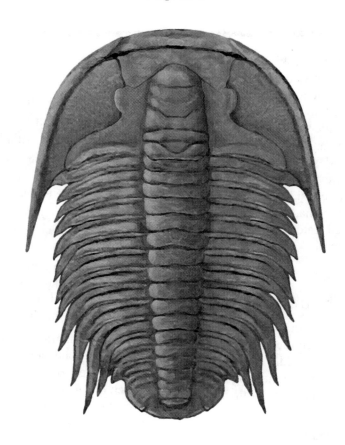

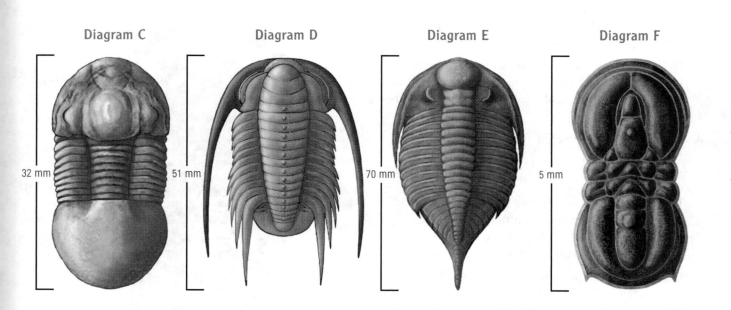

**Diagram C**

32 mm

**Diagram D**

51 mm

**Diagram E**

70 mm

**Diagram F**

5 mm

## PART 2: THE TRILOBITE FOSSIL

1.  Obtain a trilobite fossil and a hand lens from your teacher. As mentioned in Part 1, your fossil may not be complete.

2.  Which sections are present in your fossil? _____

3.  Examine the fossil closely, using the hand lens. Pay close attention to the cephalon region if present.

4.  Are the eyes simple or compound? (Look at an insect eye for comparison; insects have compound eyes.)

    _____

5.  Does it have a *genal spine*? _____

6.  Do you think your fossil is of a molted exoskeleton or of the whole organism? Why? _____

    _____

7.  If there is much rock with your fossil, you may find fossils of other trilobites or other organisms. Are there other fossils present? If so, what do you think they are? Why?

    _____

    _____

8.  Many living arthropods experience changes in the shape of their bodies each time they molt. Assuming that this also occurred with trilobite molting, how does this affect conclusions you made about your fossil?

    _____

    _____

9.  In the space below, draw your trilobite as if it were flat and include as much detail as possible. Be careful not to draw details that you cannot see. Label the parts.

## PART 3: IDENTIFICATION OF TRILOBITES

There are three to nine orders in the subphylum called Trilobita, depending on the characteristics used for classification. Five of the orders included in most classifications are listed below. Read the description of each subgroup and decide to which subgroup the trilobites in Diagrams C–F belong. Place the correct subgroup name in the blank below the respective diagram. (*Note*: One subgroup is not represented.)

*Agnostida*: small (total body length is 13 mm or less); 2–3 thoracic segments; blind (no eyes); no facial sutures

*Redlichiida*: large semicircular cephalon with genal spines; numerous thoracic segments (up to 44); crescent-shaped eyes; small pygidium

*Corynexochida*: large semicircular cephalon usually with spines; 5–11 thoracic segments; pygidium nearly the same size as the cephalon or only slightly smaller; eyes generally elongated

*Phacopida*: facial sutures extend from the front of the cephalon, to the eyes, to the rear of the shield; 8–19 thoracic segments; large- to medium-size pygidium

*Ptychopariida*: more than three thoracic segments; eyes present or absent; blunt pleural spines (Any that do not fit the other descriptions fall into this order.)

## Summing Up

1. To what animal phylum do trilobites belong? _____

2. To what does the name *trilobite* refer? _____

3. Name the three body sections of trilobites. _____

   _____

4. In what type of rock (sedimentary, igneous, metamorphic) are trilobite fossils found? _____

   _____

5. Of what kind of material was your trilobite fossil composed? _____

   _____

6. When using your hand lens and making a drawing, what did you observe about your trilobite that you did not observe without the hand lens?

   _____

7. What kind of information do you think you could obtain from a live trilobite that you could never get from fossils?

   _____

# 16 MOUNTAINS AND HIGH HILLS

### Applications

## 16A Elevation, Actual Height, and Relief

*Directions*: Write your responses in the spaces provided.

1. Mount Shasta, in northern California, has an elevation of 4317 m. If the elevation of the surrounding country is 2149 m, what is the actual height of Mount Shasta?

   _____

2. Communism Peak, in Tajikistan, has an elevation of 7495 m. If its summit is 5697 m above the surrounding country, what is the elevation of the surrounding country?

   _____

3. Does Mount Shasta or Communism Peak look higher compared to the surrounding country?

   _____

4. If the elevation of the surrounding country is 1341 m and the actual height of Mt. Ushba, in the country of Georgia, is 3353 m, what is the elevation of Ushba?

   _____

5. Mount Logan, in the Yukon Territory of Canada, has an elevation of 5959 m. If the elevation of the surrounding country is 772 m, what is the actual height of Mount Logan?

   _____

6. The lowest point in the Himalayan range is 305 m above sea level. The highest point, Mount Everest, is 8848 m above sea level. What is the relief of this region?

   _____

7. One point in California's Death Valley is 86 m below sea level. Less than 160 km away is Mt. Whitney, 4418 m above sea level. What is the relief of this region?

   _____

Consult the figure below for Questions 8 and 9.

8. What is the elevation of the highest point?

   _____

9. From which direction could a person climb to the highest point more easily?

   _____

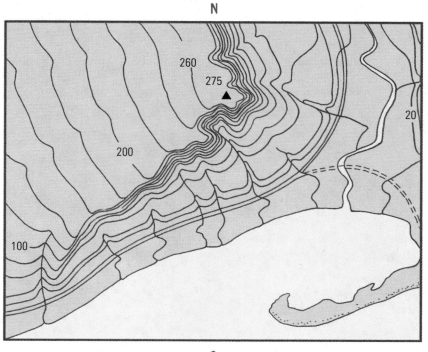

Applications

# 16B Types of Mountains

*Directions*: Match the following types of mountains associated with the words and phrases below. Indicate your answers by writing the proper letters in the blanks provided.

_____ 1. Terminal moraine

_____ 2. Probably formed by waters of the Flood flowing off the continent

_____ 3. Sierra Nevada in California

_____ 4. Mount Monadnock, New Hampshire

_____ 5. Anticline, syncline, and monocline

_____ 6. Eskers

_____ 7. Narrow, flat-topped hills with steep, nearly vertical sides

_____ 8. Drumlins

_____ 9. Igneous materials piled up or pushed out of a vent

_____ 10. Buttes and mesas

_____ 11. Domes and basins

_____ 12. Joints and faults

_____ 13. Could be caused by plate tectonics

_____ 14. Great Basin and Range Province of Nevada

_____ 15. Sand dunes

a. Depositional
b. Erosional
c. Fold
d. Fault-block

Applications
# 16C Describing Mountains

*Directions*: In the word puzzle below, write the words that are described by the following statements. Each term is related to types of mountains.

1.  Terminal _____ are ridges of rock debris that glaciers push into a pile at their front edge.

2.  One of the simplest geologic folds is the _____.

3.  A crack along which there has been slippage is a/an _____.

4.  A syncline that is roughly as long as it is wide is called a/an _____.

5.  _____ are narrow, flat-topped hills formed by erosion.

6.  A/An _____ is also called a tableland.

7.  _____ are elongated, streamlined hills deposited by glaciers.

8.  A/An _____ is a crack in a rock where there has been no slippage.

9.  _____ are broad, flat-topped hills remaining from the dissection process of erosion.

Applications
# 16D Formation of Mountains (Orogeny)

*Directions*: Write your response in the spaces provided.

1. Uniformitarian geologists use the overthrust theory to explain why "old" rocks are found on top of "young" rocks. Describe this theory and list any arguments that can be used to refute it.

_____

_____

_____

_____

_____

_____

_____

_____

_____

2. How do geologists believe mountain ranges formed? Describe the uniformitarian explanation and then give one creationary theory.

_____

_____

_____

_____

_____

_____

_____

_____

_____

Investigation

# 16E Making a Model and Relief Map of a Mountain

A map that indicates altitude and landforms by color, shading, or some other device is called a relief map. For more precise elevation information, maps are printed with contour lines. An elevation contour line connects all points on the earth's surface that are at the same elevation above a reference height—usually considered mean sea level. Contour lines on the map are labeled with their elevations. Where lines are close together, only every fifth or tenth line may be labeled. This investigation will help you to see and understand the contour lines on a relief map. The diagram below will give you an idea of how a contour relief map should look.

## Goal
Make and interpret a contour relief map.

## Materials
modeling clay, waterproof (plasticene or equivalent)

dishpan, deep

ruler, plastic metric (must be at least as long as the dishpan is deep)

beaker, 250 mL to 1 L (or water pitcher)

water

pencil, clay tool, or old ballpoint pen

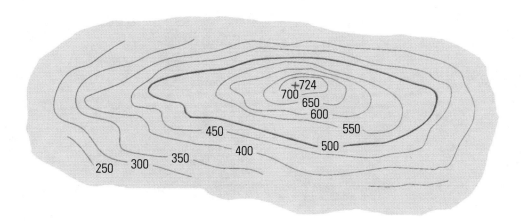

## Procedure

1. Fashion a mountain approximately 10–15 cm high out of modeling clay. The model should be no higher than the height of the dishpan. Make one side of the mountain noticeably steeper than the other. Try to give it interesting features. If you'd like, you can even give it two peaks instead of one.

2. Place the mountain model in the dishpan.

3. Tape the ruler to the inside of the dishpan, oriented vertically with 0 cm end on the floor of the dishpan.

4. Using the beaker, pour water into the dishpan to a height of approximately 1 cm.

5. Using the point of a pencil, clay tool, or ballpoint pen, mark a line all the way around the mountain at the water line.

6. Add another centimeter of water and draw another contour line at the water line.

7. Repeat the contour line drawing steps until the entire mountain is underwater.

8. Carefully pour the water out of the container and observe the mountain from directly above.

9. Draw a contour map of the model as accurately as you can in the space on the following page. Include the elevation centimeters to show the level of each line.

## Summing Up

1. Where are the lines on your relief map more closely spaced? _____
   _____
   _____

2. What does the spacing of the close lines tell you about the features of the mountain? _____
   _____
   _____

3. How would the summit of the mountain be represented on your map? _____
   _____
   _____

4. How would a contour relief map of a mountain be valuable to scientists? _____
   _____
   _____
   _____
   _____

Investigation

## 16F Making a Profile Map of a Mountain

A relief map shows you the elevation levels of a mountain as observed from above the mountain. This investigation will help you to construct a profile of the mountain from a contour relief map, showing its vertical appearance as if you were observing it from the side.

### Procedure

#### PART 1

1. Note the contour relief map of a mountain provided below. Observe the line drawn horizontally through the peak of the mountain. This line will be called the *profile reference line* for this investigation. Also observe that the elevation of each contour line is recorded on the map.

2. Place the index card so that its short side is exactly on and parallel to the 400 m line in the drawing area, and its long side intersects the profile line on the contour map. Slide the card one way or the other until it lies on the intersection of the profile reference line and the first closed contour line at the right side of the map. Lightly draw a vertical line from that elevation point down to the corresponding numbered line on the elevation scale beneath the drawing. Mark a dot at this intersection point on the applicable elevation scale line.

3. Move the index card in to the next contour line (50 m higher in elevation) where it intersects the

**Goal**
Construct a profile of a mountain, using a relief map.

**Materials**
pencil
index card, 3 × 5 in.

profile reference line. Lightly draw another vertical line down to the corresponding line on the elevation scale and mark a dot.

4. Continue to move the index card across the relief map, ensuring that the vertical edge of the index card remains perpendicular to the profile reference line. Carefully draw light vertical lines down to the corresponding heights on the elevation scale for each contour and mark dots on the appropriate elevation lines. Include all the points where a contour line intersects the profile reference line. Also include the point that represents the summit of the mountain, which falls between two contour elevations. Estimate the distance based on the summit's height between the last closed contour line and the next contour elevation.

5. Carefully connect the marks with a smooth line from left to right.

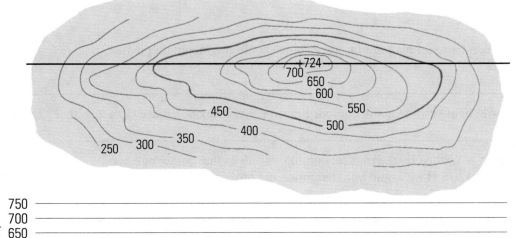

# PART 2

1. In the space below, make up a relief map of an imaginary mountain. You could also include a depression at the base of the mountain; then raise the elevation back to ground level. Include numbers for the height of elevation on each contour line. (The numbers should be within the range of the elevation scale below.)

2. Carefully draw a straight profile reference line from left to right through the main peak of your mountain.

3. Follow the procedure listed in Part 1 to draw a profile of the mountain you have created.

Elevation (in meters)

750
700
650
600
550
500
450
400
350
300
250

## Summing Up

1. If the contour lines on a relief map are far apart, how should the mountain profile look at that point?

_____

2. What does a profile help you see about contour lines on a relief map that are close together? _____

_____

3. A certain mountain is formed by the intersection of two ridges that come together at an angle of about 120°. How would you determine the profile of the mountain along these two ridges?

_____

_____

_____

_____

4. Why would contour maps and profile diagrams be important for geologists and engineers? _____

_____

Investigation
# 16G Topographic Maps

A *topographic map* is a map that represents the three-dimensional shape of the earth's surface. The features displayed on a topographic map are many. They include *relief* (differences in height from one point to the next), *water features* (lakes, streams, swamps, and the like), and *manmade features* (roads, bridges, tunnels, railroad tracks, landing strips, and buildings). Each map covers a *quadrangle* bounded by parallels of latitude on the north and south and by meridians of longitude on the east and west. Each quadrangle has its own name to identify it, such as "Greenwood, MI Quadrangle." The scale of the "topo map" is chosen to display the details of its terrain to the best advantage. A typical scale is 1:24,000; in this scale every distance in the real world is 24,000 times as large as the same distance measured on the map.

Relief is shown by means of contour lines. Contour lines are lines of equal elevation. If you were to walk along a contour line, you would move neither up nor down. You would stay at the same elevation. Notice the following facts about contour lines:

1. Theoretically, every contour line is a closed curve. That is, if you could follow it far enough, you would eventually come back to your starting point. But often only part of the line shows on the map you are using. You might need several maps placed together to trace a given line all the way back to your starting point.

2. Contour lines never cross each other, though two or more lines might merge together as they pass along the face of a cliff.

3. Closely spaced contour lines indicate a steep slope; widely spaced lines indicate a gentle slope.

4. Roughly circular contour lines, one inside the other, indicate a high point such as a rise, a hill, or a mountain. The same pattern, but with a number of short lines pointing inward from each contour line, indicates a depression.

## Goal
Use a section of an actual USGS topographic map to develop proficiency in map reading.

## Materials
ruler
drafting dividers

5. When contour lines cross a stream, they tend to bend in the shape of a "V." The point of the "V" is always in the upstream direction. For rivers flowing over relatively level terrain, the "V" shape may be flattened.

6. The vertical spacing between contour lines is called the *contour interval* of the map (abbreviated C.I.). A commonly used contour interval is 20 feet, or 5 m for metric maps, but different values are used, depending on the local situation and the map series.

7. Every fifth contour is drawn darkly; the remaining lines are drawn lightly. For example, if the contour interval is 20 feet, the 100 ft, 200 ft, and so on, lines are dark; whereas the 20 ft, 40 ft, 60 ft, and 80 ft lines are light. The dark lines are called *index contours*, and they make map reading easier.

8. The difference in elevation between the highest and lowest points in a given area is called the *maximum relief* of the area.

9. Appendix B7 provides a listing of most topographic map symbols used on United States Geological Survey (USGS) topo maps.

## Procedure and Observations

Study the map of the Passadumkeag, Maine region, taking note of the following features.

1. The Penobscot River runs roughly north and south throughout the western part of the map. What is the name of the largest island in the river visible on this map?

   _____

2. Note that highways have been built on either side of the river, roughly parallel to it. What are the route numbers of these highways? What kind of highways are they?

   _____

3. In what direction does the Penobscot River flow? (*Hint*: Look for the direction of the "V" in the contour line near where Lancaster Brook enters the river. There is also an arrow indicating flow on the map.)

   _____

4. Note the roughly north-south coursing track of the Maine Central Railroad east of the Penobscot River. If you were to take a train from Passadumkeag to Olamon, what land and vegetation would you see to the east during the first half of the trip?

   _____

5. Find Vinegar Hill near the upper right-hand corner of the map.

   What is the elevation of the highest point of the hill? _____

   How high is it above Cold Stream Pond? _____

6. An esker is a long, narrow ridge of gravel and sediment deposited by a stream flowing in or under a glacier. Enfield Horseback is probably an esker. Does it rise above or sink below the surrounding terrain? How do you know?

   _____

   _____

7. What is the contour interval of the map? _____

   What is the scale of the map? _____

8. The distance scale of this map is provided at the bottom. Using a ruler and a pair of drafting dividers, determine the approximate aerial distance from the middle of Socs Island to the highest point on Vinegar Hill in miles and kilometers.

   _____

9. Given that the Passadumkeag River is a tributary (feeder stream) of the Penobscot River, in which direction does it flow?

   _____

10. What is the maximum relief of Passadumkeag Township? Note that its western border is located in the river.

    Highest point:

    _____

    Lowest point: (Find the lowest-numbered contour line in the south-west corner of the township.)

    _____

    Maximum relief: (Subtract the two numbers recorded above.)

    _____

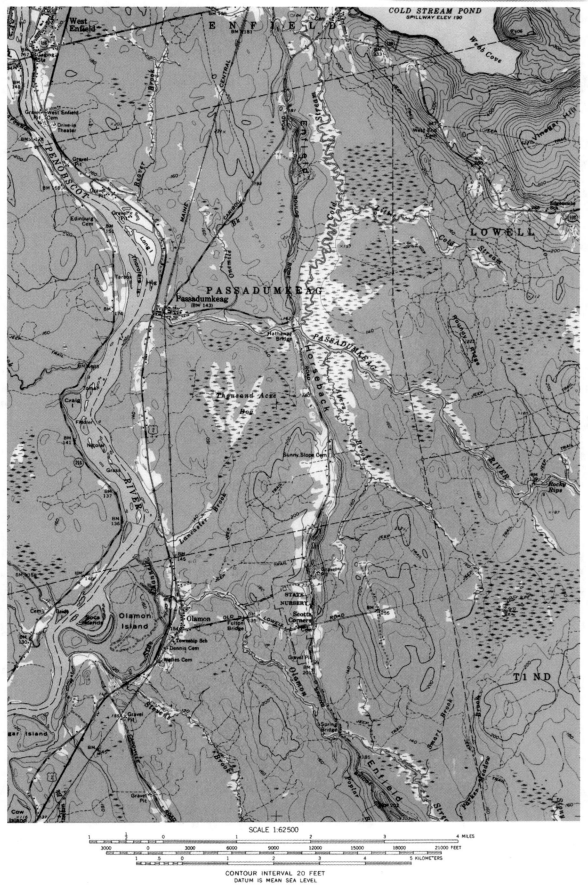

SCALE 1:62500

CONTOUR INTERVAL 20 FEET
DATUM IS MEAN SEA LEVEL

Passadumkeag Township and Environs (part of USGS Passadumkeag Quadrangle, Maine, 1960, Scale 1:62,500)

Investigation
# 16H Mountains

The map for this exercise covers a portion of north-western Montana. The name *Montana* comes from the Spanish word meaning "mountainous." Quite fittingly, mountains are prominent on both the state flag and state seal of Montana. The western part of the state is characterized by especially rugged terrain. Its elevation is so great that many permanent glaciers are found in the region.

The topographic map used here comes from the top center of the Saint Mary Quadrangle, Montana, USGS 1:100,000 . It shows the northeast corner of Glacier National Park. Its northern boundary coincides with the Canadian border. Included on the map is Chief Mountain, discussed in the Facet on page 423. This mountain is a result of the alleged Lewis Overthrust. Read the Facet carefully before proceeding with this investigation. This reading will give you important background information needed for the second part of the investigation.

## Goals

Study some of the distinctive features of a mountainous region from a topographic map.

Improve proficiency reading a topographic map.

Study the particulars of the so-called Lewis Overthrust and calculate the weight of material that is claimed to have been involved in the eastward movement of "older" rock over "younger" rock.

## Materials

calculator
ruler
drafting dividers

## Procedure

### PART 1: MAP STUDY

1. The Canadian border runs along the top of the map from corner to corner. Using your dividers and the map scale, about how far south from the border is Chief Mountain located in kilometers?

   _____

2. Give the elevation of the summit of mountain peaks listed below. If a summit elevation is not provided on the map, give the elevation interval that contains the summit represented by the highest contour line visible on the map. The first peak is done as an example.

   a. Chief Mountain __2760 m (height not shown)__

   b. Mount Wilbur _____

   c. Mount Cleveland _____

   d. Mount Cannon _____

   e. Yellow Mountain _____

   f. Mount Grinnel _____

   g. Allen Mountain _____

3. Give the elevation of each of the following bodies of water:

   Elizabeth Lake _____

   Lake Sherburne _____

   Glenns Lake _____

   Iceberg Lake _____

   McDonald Creek as it leaves the map in the lower left corner of the page (Use the last contour line it crosses.)

   _____

4. Assume that Questions 2 and 3 contain the highest and lowest elevations of the region covered by the map.

   a. What is the maximum relief of the area?

      _____

   b. Express this figure in kilometers; in miles.

      _____

5. Note the road in the lower left-hand portion of the map. It has a distinctive feature called a "switchback" (hairpin turn), which results from its having been built to gain height along a very steep slope. What name has been given to the place where the road crosses the Continental Divide?

   _____

6. What is the contour interval of the map? _____

   Is this a large or a small value for the contour interval? Why? _____

   _____

7. Locate Wynn Mountain. On which side is it steepest? _____

   Estimate the elevation of its summit, assuming that it is halfway between contour lines. _____

8. Canyon Creek is located just to the west of Wynn Mountain. Judging by the relative elevation of Cracker Lake and Lake Sherburne, does the water in the creek flow north or south?

   _____

9. A number of small glaciers are located in this part of the country. What is the name of the largest glacier shown on the map?

   _____

10. Using the scale of kilometers, determine the aerial distance from the summit of Mount Siyeh (south of Siyeh glacier) to the summit of Chief Mountain; give the distance in miles, also.

    _____

## PART 2: STUDY OF ALLEGED OVERTHRUST

1. The amount of material supposedly involved in the overthrust is given on page 423. Use the metric system of measurement in your calculations. The block of rock material allegedly measured 560 km from north to south, had an average width of 36.2 km, and had a thickness of 3.04 km. Find the volume of the material in cubic kilometers by multiplying these three numbers together:

   560 km $\times$ 36.2 km $\times$ 3.04 km = _____ km³

2. There are 1000 meters in a kilometer. Find out how many cubic meters there are in a cubic kilometer by cubing the number 1000 m/km:

   (1000 m/km)³ = _____ m³/km³

3. Multiply this number by the number you obtained in step 1 to get the total volume of the material in cubic meters:

   _____ $\times$ _____ = _____ m³

4. Assume that the rock had a specific gravity of 2.75. A cubic meter of water has a mass of $1.00 \times 10^3$ kilograms. Find the mass of a cubic meter of the rock by multiplying these two numbers together:

   _____ $\times$ _____ = _____ kg/m³

5. Multiply the answer from step 3 by the answer from step 4 to get the total mass of the rock in kilograms:

   _____ $\times$ _____ = _____ kg

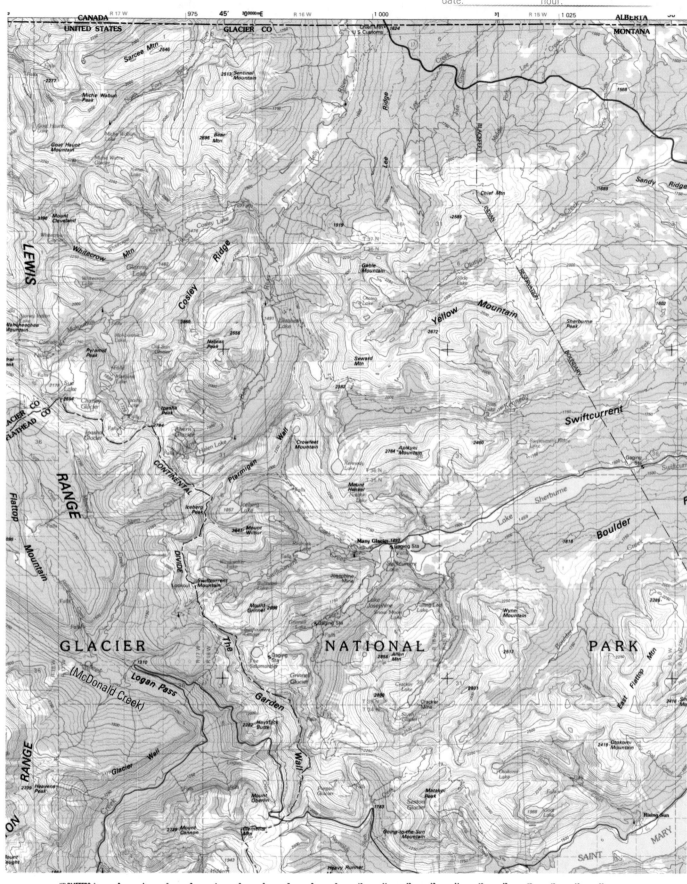

Chief Mountain Map (part of USGS Saint Mary Quadrangle, Montana, 1981. Scale 1:100,000 metric; Contour Interval 50 meters)

6. There are 1000 kilograms in a metric ton. Divide your answer from step 5 by 1000 to give the mass of the rock in metric tons:

$$\frac{\rule{3cm}{0.4pt}}{1000 \text{ kg/T}} = \underline{\hspace{4cm}} \text{ metric tons}$$

7. Express your answer in trillions of metric tons:

   _____ trillion metric tons

## Observations

1. According to the Facet, what would have happened if this immense amount of rock moved 56 km (35 mi) to the east as the theory demands?

   _____

   _____

   _____

2. The material that supposedly moved to the east is Precambrian limestone. The underlying material is Cretaceous shale. According to Investigation 15E, what is the *minimum* number of years this finding would remove from the geologic time scale?

   _____

## Summing Up

1. What factor in this terrain sustains year-round glaciers? _____

2. A good theory allows the scientist to make specific predictions about data from subsequent observations. When the observations result in data vastly different from that predicted by the theory, what does that tell you about the theory?

   _____

   _____

3. What physical evidence of overthrusting is absent in the Chief Mountain region?

   _____

   _____

4. In several parts of this map the contour lines are so close that no space can be seen between them. What does it indicate when two or more contour lines actually coincide?

   _____

   _____

5. Look up the definition of *continental divide* in your dictionary. Does this map seem to bear out the truth of its definition?

   _____

   _____

   _____

# 17 EARTHQUAKES AND VOLCANOES

## 17A Earthquake Effects

*Directions*: Listed below are ten statements concerning earthquakes. In the spaces provided, write *True* if the statement is true and *False* if the statement is false. For *False* answers, state why the answer is false in the blanks provided.

_____ 1. A tsunami is an earthquake-induced ocean wave.

_____

_____

_____ 2. The epicenter is the true center of the earthquake activity.

_____

_____

_____ 3. The Richter scale goes from 1 to 9.

_____

_____

_____ 4. The Richter scale rates the energy released by an earthquake.

_____

_____

_____ 5. Each whole number on the Richter scale has ten times as much energy as the next lower whole number.

_____

_____

_____ 6. The epicenter is the place on the earth's surface where an earthquake's energy is usually the greatest.

_____

_____

_____ 7. If an earthquake with a magnitude of 3 occurred in your area, the residents would be able to sense it.

_____

_____

_____ 8. Some of the geologic effects of earthquakes include landslides, vertical displacement, and horizontal displacement.

_____

_____

_____ 9. Richtergraphs are instruments that detect and record earth waves.

_____

_____

_____ 10. The greatest magnitude that has ever been recorded for an earthquake is 8.6.

_____

_____

Applications
# 17B Earth Waves

*Directions*: Fill in the earth-wave chart with the correct information. Two answers have been given to you.

| | P Waves | S Waves | L Waves |
|---|---|---|---|
| Complete name | Primary | | |
| Speed | | | |
| Amplitude | | Larger than P waves | |
| Travel route | | | |
| Ability to pass through core | | | |

Applications
## 17C Volcano Structure

*Directions*: Label the drawing of the volcano by supplying the missing terms or definitions.

1. Volcano

_____

_____

_____

_____

_____

2. _____

Molten rock that has
come to the surface

8. Crater

_____

_____

_____

_____

_____

3. Parasitic cone

_____

_____

_____

_____

_____

7. _____

Layered structure of
lava, ash, or a combi-
nation of the two that
was built up by suc-
cessive eruptions

6. _____

Cylindrical opening
that connects a source
of molten rock with
the surface of the
earth

4. _____

The source of magma
at the bottom of the
vent

5. _____

Molten rock beneath
the earth's surface

Applications
# 17D Volcano Activity

*Directions*: Below are several groups of words. In each group, three of the four words (or phrases) are related to one another. Draw a line through the unrelated word and then write a sentence using the remaining related words. Your sentence should show how the words are related. You may slightly change the form of the word in your sentence (for example, *volcano* to *volcanoes*, *eruption* to *erupts*).

1. volcano / structure / activity / pumice _____

_____

2. lava / shield / debris / volcano _____

_____

3. cinder cone / carbon dioxide / ejection / debris _____

_____

4. lava / composite / ash and cinders / dormant _____

_____

5. Mauna Loa / Mount Etna / Fuji / Mayon _____

_____

6. eruption / ashes / unlikely / extinct _____

_____

7. Mauna Loa / active / Vesuvius / Mount Mazama _____

_____

8. dormant / crater / volcano / eruption _____

_____

9. oxygen / water vapor / carbon dioxide / sulfur dioxide _____

_____

10. dormant / Mauna Kea / Mount Shasta / Mt. Tambora _____

_____

Identify each type of volcano in the diagrams by writing its name in the blank next to the corresponding letter.

A

11. A _____

12. B _____

13. C _____

Applications

# 17E  Famous Volcanoes

*Directions*: Read each of the following descriptions and decide which famous volcano is being described. Then indicate your answers by writing the proper letter(s) in the blanks provided.

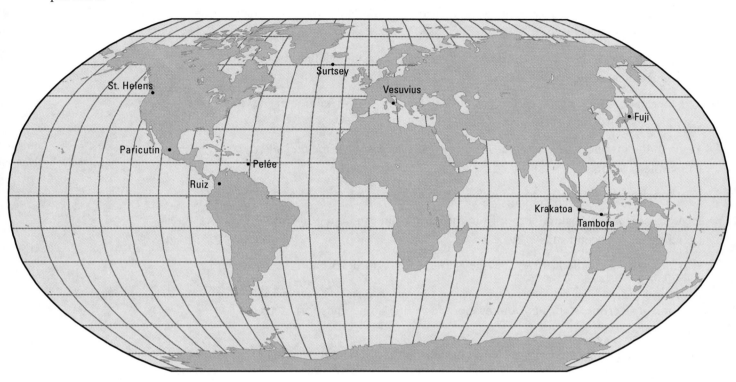

_____ 1. Located in Italy

_____ 2. Located on Martinique

_____ 3. Located in Indonesia

_____ 4. Located in Mexico

_____ 5. Located near Iceland

_____ 6. Killed 25,000 to 40,000 inhabitants—only two survivors

_____ 7. Buried the nearby town of Pompeii

_____ 8. A composite volcano located in Japan

_____ 9. Formed a new island

_____ 10. Largest known volcanic eruption

_____ 11. A mountain 430 m higher than the original cornfield

_____ 12. Rose from the ocean floor in recent historical times

_____ 13. Located in the Alpine-Himalayan belt

_____ 14. Located in the Circum-Pacific belt

_____ 15. Caused mudslides that buried thousands of people

_____ 16. Located in Washington State

_____ 17. Caused an explosion that was heard over 4800 km (3000 mi) away

a. Mount Fuji
b. Krakatoa
c. Mount Pelée
d. Mount St. Helens
e. Nevado del Ruiz
f. Paricutín
g. Surtsey
h. Tambora
i. Vesuvius

Applications
# 17F  Heated Ground Water

*Directions*: In each of the following statements, circle the correct choice in the parentheses.

1. A (geyser / geyserite) is a thermal spring that forcibly ejects its water from the ground at intervals.

2. (Japan / Italy) was the first country to experiment with using geothermal energy to produce electricity.

3. The thermal gradient of the earth averages (30 °C / 30 °F) per kilometer into the crust.

4. Vents in the ground where steam and other vapors or gases escape are called (fumaroles / lahars).

5. (Carbon dioxide / Oxygen) escaping from fumaroles can be dangerous.

6. Heating homes with natural steam from the earth is an example of the use of (geothermal / geocentric) energy.

7. A whitish deposit called (travertine / geyserite) often appears around the opening of a geyser.

8. (Tephra / Travertine) deposits from evaporating water sometimes form terraces on the sides of hills.

9. When heated ground water is carried to the surface as a liquid, it becomes a (fumarole / hot spring).

10. (Algae / Mosses) growing on the travertine around hot springs color the terraces red, blue, and brown.

# 17G Seismoscope

Seismographs are sensitive scientific instruments designed to measure and record the shaking of the earth during earthquakes. A seismoscope is similar to a seismograph but only indicates when an earthquake occurs. It does not produce a record of the quake. In this investigation, you will make a simple seismoscope.

## Setting Up

1. Set up the ring stand and clamp the base to one table with the C-clamp. Secure the right-angle support clamp near the top of the ring stand rod; then secure the dowel rod in the clamp. The dowel rod should extend over the second table. (See the figure.)

2. Strip 3 cm of insulation from each end of all three wires.

3. Attach the fishing sinker about 4 cm from the end of one wire. The bare wire should extend beyond the sinker. The sinker is the "inertial mass" of the instrument.

4. Tie the length of wire with the sinker to the dowel so that the weighted end hangs 2–3 mm above the second desktop. (Adjust the height by adjusting the ring-stand clamp.) Connect the free end of this wire to one of the battery terminals (the battery and lamp socket should be on the first desk).

5. Connect one end of the second wire to the other battery terminal and the other end of the same wire to one of the terminals on the light socket.

6. Bend the stripped portion of one end of the remaining third wire into a small circular loop (5–7 mm in diameter). Bend the loop so that it is perpendicular

## Goal
Make and demonstrate a simple seismoscope.

## Materials
desks or tables, same height (2)
ring stand
C-clamp
right angle support clamp
dowel rod, ¼ in.
dry-cell battery, 6 V
socket for 6 V light bulb
insulated wire, 0.5–1 m lengths (3)
fishing sinker (1–6 oz) (the heavier the better)
light bulb, 6 V
modeling clay (plasticene)

to the long part of the wire. Carefully insert the hanging wire through the loop; then secure the loop to the second table with a piece of clay. When all pieces are assembled and stationary, the bare end of the hanging wire should be through but not touching any part of the bare wire loop.

7. Connect the free end of the third wire to the free terminal on the light socket.

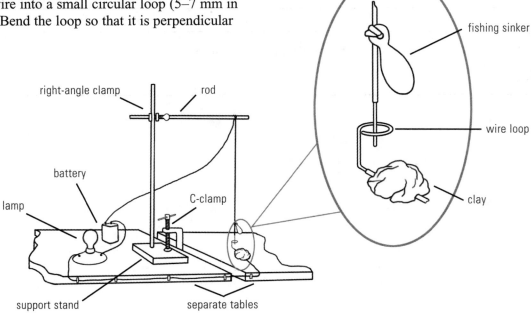

right-angle clamp    rod

battery

lamp    C-clamp

support stand    separate tables

fishing sinker

wire loop

clay

## Procedure

1. Gently bump the second table. What happens? _____
   _____
   _____

2. Shake the table harder. What happens? _____
   _____
   _____

3. Bump the table hard enough to move the table on the floor. What happens? _____
   _____
   _____

4. How does the flashing change with the strength of the bump? _____
   _____
   _____

## Summing Up

1. What does bumping the table represent? _____
   _____

2. Which part of the seismoscope is moving during an "earthquake," the loop
   "detector" or the inertial mass?
   _____
   _____

3. How could this seismoscope be made even more sensitive? _____
   _____
   _____
   _____

4. How could the movement of the table be permanently recorded? _____
   _____
   _____
   _____

5. What would this instrument be called if it were modified so that it could record
   earthquakes?
   _____

# 17H Finding the Epicenter of an Earthquake

Natural occurrences such as rock fractures and volcanism generate sound waves within the earth or along its surface. Such waves are usually called earthquakes. But the word *earthquake* means different things to different people. To some people it means an observable, physical shaking of the earth. To others, any source of vibration (even if it is observable only with sensitive instruments) is an earthquake. For this reason all waves within the earth shall be referred to as seismic waves, and the source of those seismic waves shall be referred to as an earthquake.

The three principal types of seismic waves are classified as either body waves or surface waves. Body waves travel within the earth and consist of two principal types—P (primary) and S (secondary) waves. Surface waves, or L waves, travel along the earth's surface.

## Goals

Determine the location of an earthquake's epicenter by using data from three seismic data stations.

Learn about relative energies of different quakes from Richter-scale ratings.

## Materials

calculator

map or atlas of the United States

drawing compass

textbook

| Date | Station | ID | LAT | LONG | Elev. (m) | P Wave hh:mm:ss (UTC) | S Wave | $M_R$ | Sensor |
|------|---------|-----|------|-------|-----------|-----------|--------|--------|--------|
| 28JUL05 | Elko, NV | ELK | 40.7448 | -115.2388 | 2210.0 | 18 : 11 : 57.8 | 18 : 12 : 55.3 | 7.8 | BB |
| 28JUL05 | Eugene, OR | EUO | 44.0294 | -123.0689 | 160.0 | 18 : 11 : 41.1 | 18 : 12 : 46.5 | 7.7 | BB |
| 28JUL05 | Sta Barbara, CA | SBC | 34.4408 | -119.7149 | 61.0 | 18 : 12 : 12.2 | 18 : 13 : 02.9 | 7.8 | BB |
| • | • | • | • | • | • | • | • | • | • |
| • | • | • | • | • | • | • | • | • | • |
| • | • | • | • | • | • | • | • | • | • |

c. On the map on the following page, use a drawing compass to draw a circle around each station with a radius equal to the distance from each station to the epicenter.

d. Find the major city nearest the intersection of the three circles, using a map or atlas. Label this city on your map.

## Procedure and Observations

1. Determine the epicenter of an earthquake from the representation of seismograph readings above. (*Note*: Each record gives the arrival time of the earthquake shock waves and the relative magnitude [Richter-scale or $M_R$] readings of the surface waves.)

This is a simulated computer monitor display of earthquake data from three seismic stations in the western United States. The times that the P and S waves were received at each station are reported in Universal Coordinated Time (UTC), which is nearly equivalent to Greenwich Mean Time (GMT).

a. Find the time between the P waves and the S waves for each station ($t_S - t_P$). Record the times in the Data Table on the following page.

b. Find the distance from each station to the epicenter, using the following formula: $d = 9.56(t_S - t_P)$. Record the distances on the Data Table.

2. Calculate the time at which the earthquake occurred at the epicenter.

a. Use the following equation to calculate the time it took for the S and P waves to reach each station.

$$\text{time of travel } (t) = \frac{\text{distance from epicenter}}{\text{speed of wave}} = \frac{d}{v}$$

Record your times on the Data Table. (*Note*: Assume that the speed of a P wave is 8.5 km/s and that the speed of an S wave is 4.5 km/s.)

b. Subtract the time of travel from the time of the reading (displayed on the computer monitor) to obtain the time of occurrence at the epicenter. Perform this calculation for both the S and P waves for each station. Record the times of occurrence on the Data Table.

## Data Table

| Station | $t_S - t_P$ (s) | Distance ($d$) from epicenter (km) | Time of travel ($t$) | | Time of occurrence | |
|---|---|---|---|---|---|---|
| | | | P wave (s) | S wave (s) | P wave | S wave |
| Elko, NV | | | | | | |
| Eugene, OR | | | | | | |
| Santa Barbara, CA | | | | | | |

3. Which quake had more energy, the one reported in this investigation or one rated 6.8 on the Richter scale?

_____

How much more energy did the greater quake have? _____

_____

## Summing Up

1. What are the two main types of seismic waves? _____

_____

2. What instrument detects the amplitude and wavelength of seismic waves? _____

_____

3. What is the epicenter of an earthquake? _____

_____

# 171 Types of Volcanoes

Volcanoes are classified into three groups according to their structure: shield, cinder cone, and composite volcanoes. In this investigation you will study examples of shield and composite volcanoes.

Shield volcanoes, such as those in the Hawaiian Islands, are made up entirely of solidified lava flows. In fact, the Hawaiian Islands are composed completely of shield volcanoes that have grown upward from the floor of the Pacific Ocean. The largest of these islands, called Hawaii, is an aggregation of *five* volcanoes: Mauna Kea, Mauna Loa, Hualalai, Kohala, and Kilauea. At least two of these, Mauna Loa and Kilauea, are still active. The highest peak, Mauna Kea, is a volcano that has long been dormant. The summit of Mauna Kea, at a lofty 4205 m (13,796 ft) above sea level, is the site of important national and international astronomical observatories. If you consider the fact that there is more of the mountain *below* the surface of the water than there is above it, 6002 m (19,692 ft) below compared to 4205 m (13,796 ft) above, you can understand how the actual height of the mountain at 10,203 m (33,476 ft) is greater than the actual height of Mount Everest, 8848 m (29,028 ft). In fact, if total heights are compared, Mauna Kea rates as the world's tallest mountain. Mauna Loa is a close second at 10,172 m (33,372 ft) total height.

Composite volcanoes are a combination of shield volcanoes and cinder cones. They are built of layers of lava interbedded (alternated) with layers of cinders and ash. The largest and highest volcanic mountains are generally of this type. Some composite volcanoes begin as shield volcanoes and then gradually change their behavior as time goes on. Examples of composite volcanoes are Mounts Etna and Fuji and Mayon Volcano in the Philippines. In the United States a number of examples are found in the states that border the Pacific Ocean: Mount Shasta, Mount Rainier, Mount St. Helens, Mount Hood, Mount Lassen, and the volcanic peak in which Crater Lake is located (Mount Mazama).

One additional piece of information is needed for this investigation. A *topographic profile* is a graph that shows the side view, or outline, of a portion of the earth's surface. Usually the vertical distance is exaggerated somewhat on the graph to show the differences in elevation more clearly.

## Goals

Construct a topographic profile across the summit of Mauna Kea.

Study the distinctive features of the Mount St. Helens area.

## Materials

ruler

## Procedure and Observations

### PART 1: MAUNA KEA—A SHIELD VOLCANO

1. Look at the map of Hawaii on the next page.

2. Note the five volcanic peaks: Mauna Kea, 4205 m (13,796 ft); Mauna Loa, 4169 m (13,677 ft); Hualalai, 2521 m (8271 ft); Kohala, 1670 m (5480 ft); and Kilauea, 1248 m (4096 ft).

3. Use the grid provided to draw a topographic profile from west to east (from point *A* to point *B*, a distance of 93 km, or 58 mi) through the summit of Mauna Kea. (*Note*: Since points *A* and *B* are both at sea level, they are placed on the zero contour line.)

   a. Position a ruler parallel to the vertical solid lines.

   b. Directly below each intersection of the line *AB* with a contour line, indicated by a tick mark, mark a point on the grid. Be sure to place the point on the correct elevation line of the grid; note that each contour line on the map represents 1000 feet, and each line on the profile grid represents 1000 feet.

   c. Connect the points carefully to show the topographic profile when you have placed all twenty-seven points on the grid (not counting endpoints A and B).

   d. Divide each vertical distance by 3.5 and make a new plot under the one you have. This will give you a true picture of what the volcano looks like since the scale of the grid used here gives a 3.5:1 vertical exaggeration. (*Note*: Your new topographic profile tends to mask some of the detail. Because of this effect, some vertical exaggeration is generally used when drawing a topographic profile.)

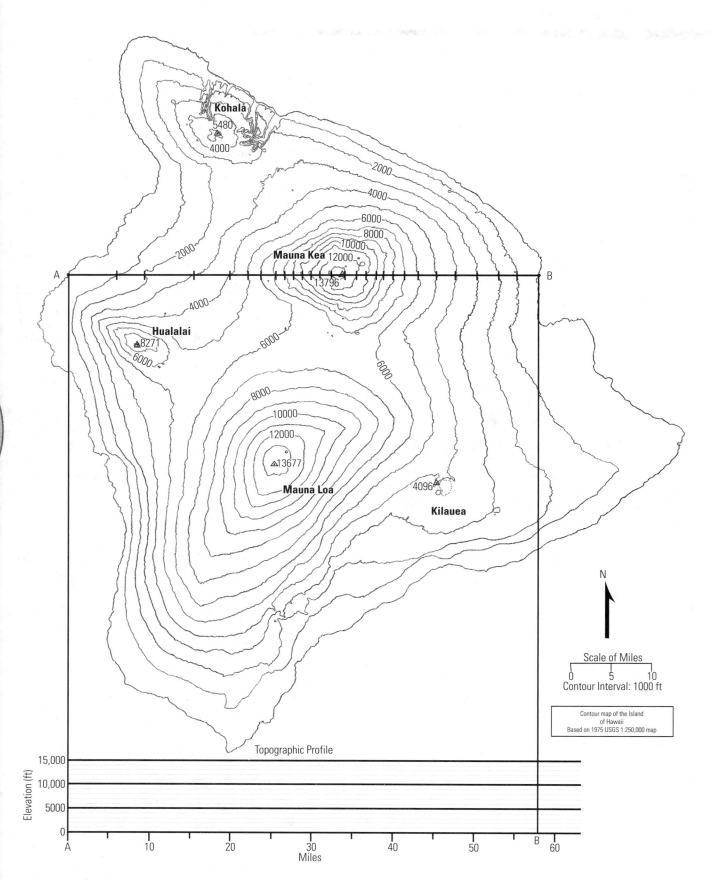

Kohala
△5480
4000

2000
4000
6000
8000
10000
Mauna Kea 12000
△13796

2000

A |||||||||||||||||||||||||||||||| B

4000

Hualalai
△8271
6000

6000

8000
10000
12000
△13677
Mauna Loa

4096△
Kilauea

N

Scale of Miles
0       5       10
Contour Interval: 1000 ft

Contour map of the Island
of Hawaii
Based on 1975 USGS 1:250,000 map

Topographic Profile

15,000

10,000

Elevation (ft)

5000

0

A          10          20          30          40          50    B   60
Miles

# PART 2: MOUNT ST. HELENS—A COMPOSITE VOLCANO

Notice that the map of Mount St. Helens on the next page shows some of the effects of the cataclysmic blast of May 18, 1980. This blast occurred after two months of seismic activity and minor eruptions of steam and ash. As can be seen from the map, the destruction was directed toward the north, northeast, and northwest of the volcano. Note that the north rim of the crater has been blown away. The stippled dark area represents landslide debris that avalanched down the mountainside at speeds of up to 240 km/h (150 mi/h). The unstippled dark areas represent mudflows. The volume of material removed from the mountain has been estimated at 3 km³ (3 billion m³, or ¾ mi³). The avalanched debris quickly dammed up streams and intruded into the southwest corner of Spirit Lake, greatly raising the level of the water in the process. Debris was carried as much as 21 km (13 mi) to the northwest by the North Fork of the Toutle River, inflicting serious damage to roads, bridges, and logging equipment along the way. All told, more than 520 km² (200 mi²) of timberland and recreational areas were devastated. The "Eruption Impact Area" label at the top of the map is located at the approximate center of the affected region.

1. Several new lakes were formed when streams were dammed by debris. These are designated by arrows with a number 3 on them. How many of these features show on the map?

   _____

2. The arrow labeled 5 shows several new islands that formed in Spirit Lake at the time of the eruption. Assuming there were none before the blast, how many new islands were formed?

   _____

3. Mount St. Helens, before the eruption, possessed a picturesque cone-shaped peak. The elevation of its summit was 2950 m. The highest point on the mountain is now 2550 m. How many meters of height did it lose?

   _____

   How many feet of height did it lose? (1 m = 3.28 ft) _____

4. The bottom of the crater is 665 m below the highest part of the south rim and 46 m below what remains of the north rim. What is the difference in heights between the north and south rims?

   In meters: _____

5. The former elevation of Spirit Lake was 975 m above sea level.

   a. What is it now? (Assume that it is halfway between contour lines.)

      _____

   b. How many meters did it increase in elevation?

      _____

   c. How many feet did it increase in elevation?

      _____

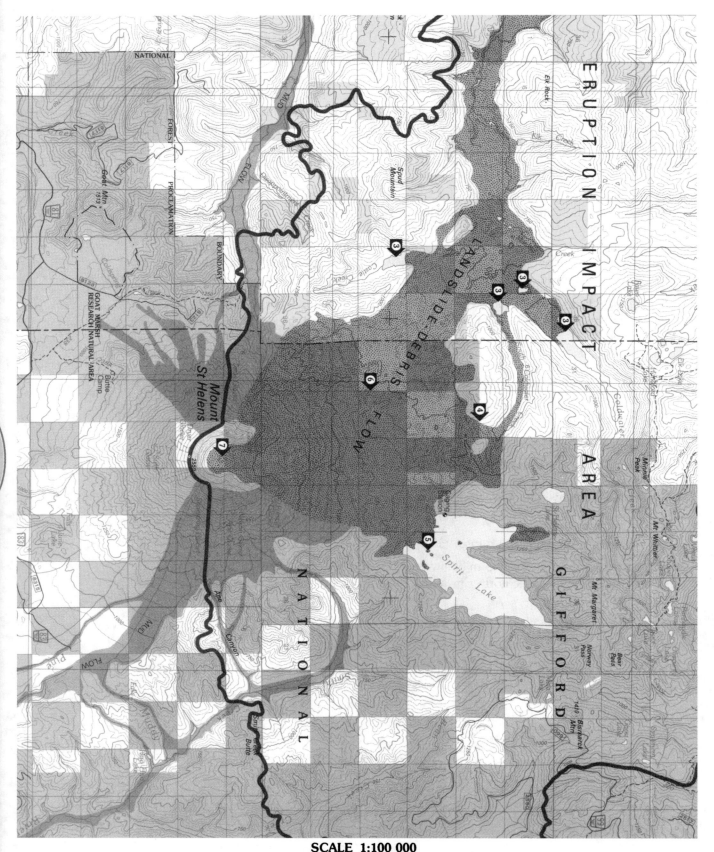

## SCALE 1:100 000
1 CENTIMETER ON THE MAP REPRESENTS 1 KILOMETER ON THE GROUND
CONTOUR INTERVAL 50 METERS

KILOMETERS

MILES

Part of Mount Saint Helens and Vicinity Map (March 1981; Scale 1:100,000; Contour Interval 50 meters)

# 18 WEATHERING, MASS WASTING, AND EROSION

### Applications
## 18A  A Degenerating Earth

*Directions*: Below are several groups of words. In each group, three of the four words (or phrases) are related to one another. Draw a line through the unrelated word and then write a sentence using the remaining related words. Your sentence should show how the words are related. You may slightly change the form of the words in your sentence (for example, *eye* to *eyes*, *fingerprint* to *fingerprinting*).

1. weathering / rock / disintegrates / streams _____
_____

2. mass wasting / streams / hills / lower _____
_____

3. disintegrates / erosion / soil / streams _____
_____

4. chemical / erosion / mechanical / weathering _____
_____

5. natural acids / mass wasting / agents / chemical weathering _____
_____

6. weathering agents / break up / dissolving / physical _____
_____

7. mechanical weathering / warmth / chemical weathering / moisture _____
_____

8. chemical weathering / hinders / rock surface / weathering agents _____
_____

9. chemical weathering / physical forces / mechanical weathering / breaks ___
_____

10. frost heaving / weathering / pushes downward / ice _____
_____

Applications
# 18B Chemical and Mechanical Weathering

*Directions*: Complete the missing words in the following statements by filling in the necessary letters. After you complete each question, find the matching number in the word puzzle below and then fill in the correct letter. The circled letters finish the sentence below that describes degenerative processes.

1. Carbonic acid and humic acid are two agents that promote
   ____ ____ ____ ____ (1) ____ ____ ____ weathering.

2. Mechanical weathering is the breaking up of rocks into smaller pieces by
   ____ ____ (2) ____ ____ ____ ____ ____ ____ ____ ____ ____ ____ ____ ____.

3. Frost ____ ____ ____ ____ ____ ____ (3) is one way that freezing water
   causes weathering.

4. Wind carries off loose material, leaving excavated areas called
   ____ ____ ____ (4) ____ ____ ____ ____.

5. Rock debris, called ____ (5) ____ ____ ____, accumulates at the base of a cliff.

6. Water (6) ____ ____ ____ ____ ____ ____ about nine percent when it freezes
   and can exert tremendous pressure within cracks and crevasses.

7. Exfoliation, a process which involves both chemical and mechanical weathering,
   extensively weathers even extremely durable materials like ____ (7) ____ ____ ____ ____ ____.

8. A ____ ____ ____ ____ ____ ____ ____ ____ ____ ____ ____ (8) ____
   is a place where all the materials have blown away, leaving only pebbles and cobbles.

9. The earth's surface is ____ ____ ____ ____ ____ ____ ____ ____ ____ ____ ____.
   　　　　　　　　　　　　　　4　6　5　7　1　8　3　5　4　5　2

Applications
# 18C Soil Science

*Directions*: Use the definitions to help unscramble the terms.

_____ 1. A fine-grained material deposited as sediment from water
LITS

_____ 2. Produced by the decomposition of leaves and other organic matter
UMUSH

_____ 3. A soil scientist
TOGEPIDLOS

_____ 4. The soil component most likely to be dominant in a region with
DASN       mainly quartz rocks

_____ 5. The soil component most likely to be predominant in a region
YALC       with mainly mica and feldspar minerals

_____ 6. An especially fertile soil, containing about equal parts of sand
MALO       and silt and about half as much clay

_____ 7. A process used by farmers in dry climates to help their crops
GATIROIRNI     grow in fertile soils

_____ 8. Chemical or organic nutrients added to the soil by farmers to
REZITREFLI     restore the nutrients that have been removed from the soil

_____ 9. A cross section of the soil
EFIPOLR

_____ 10. Layers of soil seen in Number 9
SHNOORIZ

Applications
# 18D Mass Wasting

*Directions*: Read each description carefully and decide which type of mass wasting is
being described. Then indicate your answers by writing the proper letters in the blanks
provided. Some descriptions have more than one answer.

_____ 1. A sudden catastrophic slippage caused by weakness or loss of
friction between layers of bedrock

_____ 2. Example(s) of slow mass wasting

_____ 3. Example(s) of rapid mass wasting

_____ 4. Example(s) of a debris slide

_____ 5. May occur in places having near-continuous below-freezing conditions

_____ 6. Triggered sometimes by earthquakes

_____ 7. Downhill movement of large masses of solid soil or rock as a direct result
of gravity

_____ 8. So slow that the cover of grass or other surface vegetation is not broken

_____ 9. Can be triggered or accelerated by heavy rainfall.

_____ 10. Usually involves the movement of largely unconsolidated volcanic material

a. Creep
b. Avalanche
c. Rockslide
d. Debris slide
e. Lahar
f. Rock glacier

Applications

# 18E Stream Erosion

*Directions*: Label the drawing by writing in the terms from the following list.

| | | |
|---|---|---|
| alluvial fan | headwaters (or source) | natural levees |
| base level | high-gradient stream | neck |
| delta | low-gradient stream | neck cutoff |
| drainage basin | meander | oxbow lake |
| flood plain | mouth | tributary |

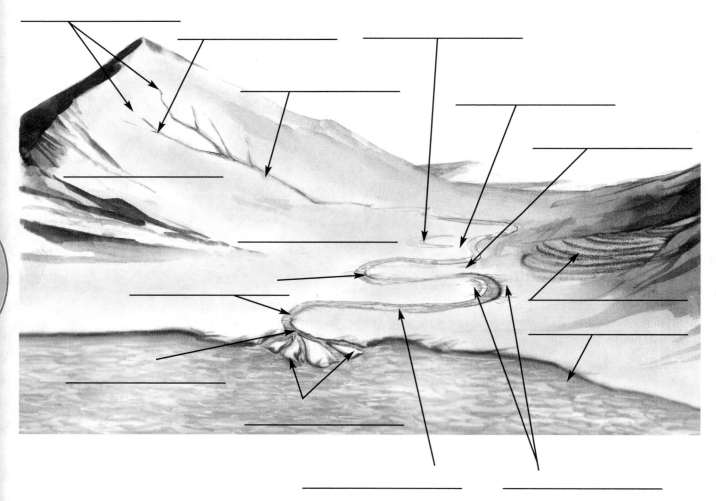

Investigation

# 18F  Soil Composition

Soil is composed of solids (rocks, sand, silt, clay), liquid (water), air, and organic matter (living and nonliving). In this investigation you will determine the amount of solids, water, and organic matter in a soil sample.

## Procedure

1. In an area where you have permission to dig, collect a volume of soil about 15 cm (6 in.) square and 15 cm deep. (Your teacher may have done this ahead of time.)

2. Place a sheet of weighing paper on a balance. Measure 10 g of the soil onto the paper, then remove the sample to your desk. Using a hand lens, carefully examine the sample.

3. Count the live animals (insects, worms, and so forth) you find and record this number in Table A.

4. Mix the 10 g sample of soil thoroughly with 250 mL of water in a graduated cylinder.

5. Allow the mixture to sit undisturbed for 5 minutes. Organic debris should float to the surface of the water, and the rocks and sand will settle to the bottom. Silt and clay will remain suspended in the water.

6. While the suspension is settling, label the beakers with a grease pencil or tape before measuring their masses. Beaker A is the larger beaker and Beakers B and C are the two smaller beakers. Then find the mass of each of the three beakers and record them in the blanks above Table A.

7. Slowly and carefully pour the cloudy water from the graduated cylinder through cheesecloth or a wire strainer into the larger beaker (A) and label it "silt, clay, and water." Do not pour out the material settled on the bottom of the graduated cylinder.

8. Place the organic debris that you filtered out into Beaker B. Label this beaker "organic debris."

### Goal

Identify and measure the various components in a soil sample.

### Materials

balance (accurate to at least 0.1 g)
paper, weighing
ruler, metric
beaker, 1 L
oven or hot plate
cheesecloth or wire strainer
small shovel
graduated cylinder, 250 mL
beakers, 250 mL (2)
hand lens

9. Refill the graduated cylinder with fresh water and thoroughly mix it with the remaining sediment. Repeat Steps 7 and 8, adding the cloudy water and organic debris to what had previously separated.

10. Repeat Step 9 until the water is relatively clear after 5 minutes of settling.

11. Transfer the remaining sediment from the graduated cylinder to the other smaller beaker (C). You may need to rinse the graduated cylinder with water to transfer all the soil. Use as little water as possible. Label this beaker "stones and sand."

12. Slowly pour off the water in Beaker C, being careful not to lose any of the stones or sand. Count the number of stones in this wet sediment that are 2–5 mm in diameter and record this number in Table A.

## TABLE A

Mass of Beaker A: _____ g     Mass of Beaker B: _____ g     Mass of Beaker C: _____ g

| Number of live animals | Mass of organic debris | Mass of rock and sand | Mass of silt, clay, and water | Number of rocks 2–5 mm in diameter |
|---|---|---|---|---|
|  | g | g | g |  |

13. Heat the beakers containing the "organic debris" (B) and "stones and sand" (C) in a 150 °C (300 °F) oven or on a hot plate until they are dry (5–20 min). Be careful not to burn the organic debris.

14. Measure the mass of each beaker with its dry contents; then subtract the mass of the empty beakers recorded in Step 6 to determine the mass of the organic debris and the stones and sand. Record these masses in Table A.

| Mass of Beaker B with dry organic material | − | Mass of empty Beaker B | = | Mass of organic material |
|---|---|---|---|---|
| _____ g | − | _____ g | = | _____ g |

| Mass of Beaker C with dry stones and sand | − | Mass of empty Beaker C | = | Mass of stones and sand |
|---|---|---|---|---|
| _____ g | − | _____ g | = | _____ g |

15. You can determine the weight of the silt, clay, and water present in the original soil sample by subtracting the weights of the organic debris and rocks and sand from the beginning weight of 10 g.

| Beginning weight of soil | − | Weight of dry organic debris | − | Weight of dry rock and sand | = | Weight of silt, clay, and water |
|---|---|---|---|---|---|---|
| 10 g | − | _____ g | − | _____ g | = | _____ g |

## Summing Up

1. What kinds of materials make up the organic matter found in the soil? _____
   _____
   _____

2. What kinds of living organisms did you find in the soil? _____
   _____
   _____

3. What might make the amount of water in different soil samples vary? _____
   _____
   _____

4. What might make the amount of living plants and animals in different soil samples vary? _____
   _____
   _____

5. How could the geographic location of soil samples affect your results? _____
   _____
   _____
   _____

6. How could the depth from which you take the soil samples affect your results? _____
   _____
   _____

## Go a Step Further

### PART 1

Dig a trench exposing all three horizons of a soil profile and repeat this investigation with samples from each horizon. Determine which horizon has the most and least of each soil component examined in the investigation.

### PART 2

Determine separate masses for the amounts of silt, clay, and water present in a soil sample. Find the mass of a sample before and after heating it to evaporate the water. The difference will be due to soil water. Determine the mass of silt and clay in a sample by evaporating the water from the "silt, clay, and water" (Beaker A) used in steps 7–10 of the Procedure. Find the mass of the beaker with the dried silt and clay and subtract the mass of the empty beaker. The difference will be the weight of only the silt and clay. Compare these masses with those obtained by subtraction in the investigation.

Investigation
# 18G Erosion

Erosion is a process that occurs slowly. In this investigation you will develop your own methods for causing erosion and then will observe their effects on a pan of sand.

## Procedure

1. Put about 5 cm of sand in one half of the dishpan. Leave the other half of the dishpan empty.

2. Create ways to move the sand to the other half of the dishpan *without directly touching the sand or dishpan.* This means that you cannot tilt the dishpan or put your fingers or a tool into the sand to push it to the other side.

3. List the ways you can move the sand without directly touching it with your hands or tools. Write this list on a separate sheet of paper.

4. Use each method and then record its effectiveness on your paper.

## Goal
Identify and compare ways by which erosion can move material.

## Materials
large dishpan
sand
water

## Summing Up

1. Which method of moving the sand worked the best? _____
_____

2. Was it possible to move the entire pile of sand? _____
_____

3. What do your observations tell you about erosion that is going on today in the land around you?
_____
_____
_____
_____

4. What do your observations lead you to conclude about the effects of a global Flood as the bodies of water over the continents flowed rapidly back into the ocean basins?
_____
_____
_____
_____
_____
_____
_____

# 19 THE OCEANS AND SEAS

## 19A Wave Structure

*Directions*: Label the diagram of a typical wave below; then answer the questions that follow.

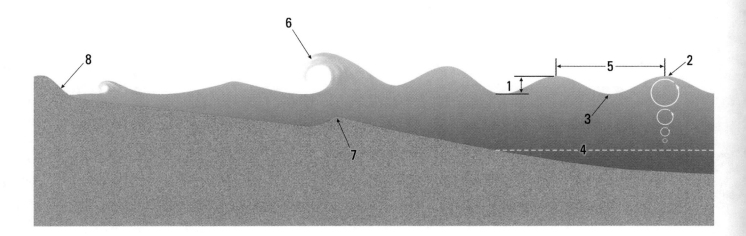

1. _____

2. _____

3. _____

4. _____

5. _____

6. _____

7. _____

8. _____

9. What causes the breaker to form at the beach? _____

_____

_____

10. Can breakers form before the wave approaches the beach? _____

11. Explain your answer to Question 10. _____

_____

_____

_____

Applications

# 19B Wave Motions

*Directions*: The descriptions listed below describe something about waves as they approach the shore. Some of the descriptions apply only to waves in deep water (including deep coastal waters), some only to waves in shallow water, and some can apply to either. Read each description carefully; then write either *shallow*, *deep*, or *both* in the blanks in front of the descriptions.

_____ 1. Diagonal approach

_____ 2. Diagonal right up to the shoreline

_____ 3. Parallel at the shoreline

_____ 4. Longshore currents develop

_____ 5. Rip currents develop

_____ 6. Refraction occurs

_____ 7. Flattened circular wave motion orbits

_____ 8. Beach drifting results

_____ 9. Breaking waves are caused only by wind

_____ 10. Wave forms a breaker

Applications
# 19C Wave Erosion and Deposition

*Directions*: The first diagram represents a rocky shoreline in which erosion occurs. The second diagram represents a sandy shoreline in which deposition occurs. Label the diagrams by supplying the missing terms or definitions; then draw a line from each term to the proper structure in the diagram.

Stack

_____

_____

_____

_____

Sea cave

_____

_____

_____

_____

_____
Mass of rock with the center eroded away forming a "bridge"

Barrier island

_____

_____

_____

_____

Tombolo

_____

_____

_____

_____

_____
A body of water partly enclosed by land; named by local convention

Bay barrier

_____

_____

_____

_____
An exposed sandbar extending into the mouth of a bay from a headland

_____
An exposed sandbar extending with a sharp bend beyond a headland

Applications
# 19D Ocean Currents

*Directions*: The map below shows the major surface ocean currents. Label the currents depicted on the map (Questions 1–6), then answer Questions 7–10.

1. _____     4. _____

2. _____     5. _____

3. _____     6. _____

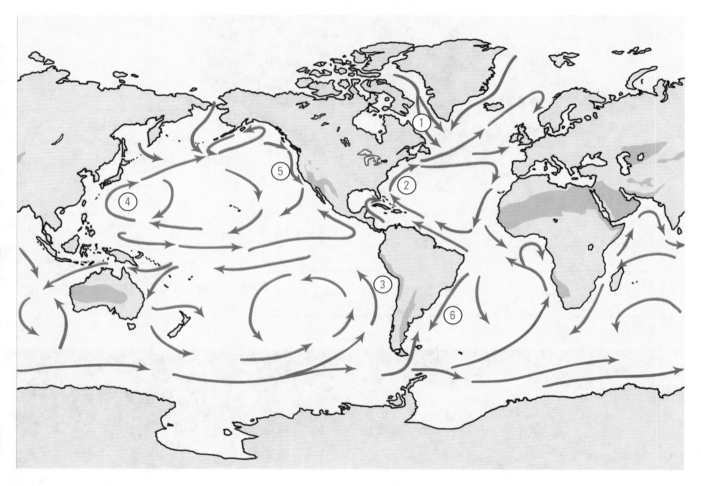

7. Would you expect the northwest coast of Africa to be influenced by cold waters or warm waters? _____
   Why? _____

8. Would you expect the southern tip of South America to be influenced by cold or warm waters? _____
   Why? _____

9. The eastern coast of the United States has warmer waters than the western coast. Why? _____
   _____
   _____

10. In which direction do the current gyres in the Northern Hemisphere flow? _____
    in the Southern Hemisphere? _____ Why? _____
    _____

# 19E Ocean Topography

*Directions*: Write the word *True* in the blank provided if the statement is true; write *False* if the statement is false. For *False* answers, state why the answer is false in the blanks provided.

_____ 1. Guyots are flat-topped seamounts.

_____

_____

_____ 2. Abyssal plains are long, relatively narrow zones of higher elevation on the ocean floors.

_____

_____

_____ 3. Scientists from nearly every scientific field study the oceans.

_____

_____

_____ 4. The ocean basins are flat and featureless.

_____

_____

_____ 5. An island arc is a long chain of volcanic islands that is usually located near the edge of a tectonic plate.

_____

_____

_____ 6. The term *seamount* refers to a submerged mountain that is situated on an abyssal plain.

_____

_____

_____ 7. The *Trieste* is the first bathysphere to descend to the deepest part of the Atlantic Ocean.

_____

_____

_____ 8. Geographically, the world ocean is divided into three major basins: the Atlantic, the Indian, and the Pacific oceans.

_____

_____

_____ 9. Today the depth of the ocean is most accurately measured by lowering a line with a lead weight attached to it to the bottom of the ocean and measuring the length of the line.

_____

_____

_____ 10. The Mid-Atlantic Ridge is an example of a guyot.

_____

_____

(continued on next page)

_____ 11. The British ship HMS *Challenger* made a four-year study of the ocean beginning in 1872.

_____

_____

_____ 12. Echo sounding is a technique that involves sending sound waves to the ocean floor and recording the time they take to return. The depth is half the calculated distance of the round trip based on the speed of sound in water.

_____

_____

_____ 13. The greatest obstacle to visiting the ocean floor is the temperature of the water.

_____

_____

_____ 14. The depth of the Mariana Trench is about 11,000 m below sea level.

_____

_____

_____ 15. The gently sloping bottom adjacent to most continental coastlines is called the continental slope.

_____

_____

Applications
# 19F  Ocean Basins

*Directions*: The diagram below represents a typical ocean basin. In each box, place the letter of the term that best describes the feature.

a. Abyssal plain
b. Canyon
c. Continent
d. Continental rise
e. Continental shelf
f. Continental slope
g. Guyot
h. Island
i. Mid-ocean ridge
j. Rift
k. Seamount
l. Trench

Applications
# 19G Coral Reefs

*Directions*: Read each of the phrases about coral reefs carefully. Decide which of the following types of coral reefs is described by each phrase. Write the proper letter in the blank in front of the phrase.

a. Fringing reef    b. Barrier reef    c. Atoll

_____ 1. A ring of low coral islands surrounding a central lagoon

_____ 2. Reefs extending from the beach low-water mark into deeper water

_____ 3. Reefs that parallel the beach but have deeper open water between them and the beach

_____ 4. The type of reef found in some of the Pacific Islands such as Wake, Midway, Bikini, and Eniwetok

_____ 5. The great reef off the coast of Australia that extends for about 2000 km

_____ 6. The type of reef that occurs along the coast of Florida and the coast of Bermuda

_____ 7. Attached to the bottom of the ocean near the shoreline, leaving very little water between the reef and the mainland

_____ 8. A coral reef surrounding the top of a volcano that has either collapsed or been carried into deeper water by the motion of the ocean floor

Applications

# 19H Oceans Review

*Directions*: Select the proper terms from the list to complete the statements below. Write your answers in the blanks provided. A term may be used only one time.

| | | | | |
|---|---|---|---|---|
| abyssal plains | cold | guyot | North Pacific | slope |
| arch | continental | height | plankton net | spit |
| atoll | density | hook | ridge | spring tide |
| autonomous | desalination | island | rip | stack |
| barrier | distillation | lagoon | rise | tide |
| bathyscaph | echo sounding | longshore | salt | tombolo |
| breaker | erosion | Mid-Atlantic | sand | upwelling |
| canyon | fringing | neap | seamount | wind |

1. In 1960 the *Trieste*, a _____, explored water over 11,000 m (36,000 ft) below sea level.

2. The _____ shelf is the part of the ocean floor that slopes gently out from the continental shoreline at most places.

3. A/An _____ connects an island to the mainland.

4. A/An _____ current exists where sediment-laden or salty water is sinking along a sloping bottom.

5. Waves erode rock on a shore and then redeposit the eroded materials in the form of _____.

6. _____ causes various shoreline features such as sea caves and sea arches.

7. The process of making seawater fit to drink is called _____.

8. The oceans bulge at high _____ because of the pull of the moon and the sun and the momentum of the ocean waters.

9. The most straightforward but less efficient way to desalinate water is the process called

_____.

10. A sandbar that extends partway across a bay from a headland is called a/an _____.

11. A ring of low coral islands surrounding a central lagoon is called a/an _____.

12. A flat-topped seamount is called a/an _____.

13. A deeply eroded valley under the sea is called a submarine _____.

14. A/An _____ is a mass of rock cut off from the mainland by erosion.

15. A drowned island or a submarine volcano is referred to as a/an _____.

16. A barrier reef is separated from the mainland by a/an _____.

17. A device used to collect drifting organisms in deep water is called a/an _____.

18. A mass of coral following a shoreline and attached to it or to an island is called a/an

_____ reef.

19. A wave that "falls over" because it is too steep is called a/an _____.

20. A sandy beach completely across the mouth of a bay is called a bay _____.

21. A sandy beach with no visible connection to the nearby mainland is a barrier _____.

22. The continental _____ slopes less severely away from the coninental slope to the ocean floor.

(continued on next page)

| | | | | |
|---|---|---|---|---|
| abyssal plains | cold | guyot | North Pacific | slope |
| arch | continental | height | plankton net | spit |
| atoll | density | hook | ridge | spring tide |
| autonomous | desalination | island | rip | stack |
| barrier | distillation | lagoon | rise | tide |
| bathyscaph | echo sounding | longshore | salt | tombolo |
| breaker | erosion | Mid-Atlantic | sand | upwelling |
| canyon | fringing | neap | seamount | wind |

23. The continental _____ is the outer edge of the continental shelf where the ocean quickly deepens.

24. Waves on large lakes or oceans are usually caused by the _____.

25. A spit with a sharp bend is called a/an _____.

26. The best-known mid-ocean ridge is the _____ Ridge.

27. A bridge-like formation left by coastal erosion is called a sea _____.

28. A/An _____ current is a strong surface current that courses through a gap in the breakers.

29. A more practical method to remove _____ from seawater is called reverse osmosis.

30. Flat, deep seafloors are called _____.

31. The _____ Current warms the climate of western Canada.

32. _____ water tends to sink.

33. A very high tide that results from an alignment of the sun, moon, and earth is called a/an _____.

34. A/An _____ tide occurs twice each month, when the moon is at the first and third quarters.

35. An unmanned submersible that is programmed to conduct research without any connection to a tending ship is called a/an _____ underwater vehicle.

36. A/An _____ occurs when cold water from the ocean bottom is forced upward to replace warmer waters that have been removed by strong prevailing winds.

37. The vertical distance from the crest of one wave to the trough of another is called the wave's _____.

38. Today oceanographers use _____ to measure the depths of the oceans.

39. A long, relatively narrow zone of higher elevation on the seafloor is called a mid-ocean _____.

40. A/An _____ current flows parallel to the shore.

# Investigation
# 191 Desalting Seawater

## Procedure and Observations

*Note*: If the distilled water is going to be tasted at the end of this procedure, ensure that all glassware and hose used have never been in contact with poisonous chemicals and have been thoroughly washed.

1. Obtain 3.5 g of salt (NaCl).

2. Pour the salt into the Erlenmeyer flask.

3. Measure out 100 mL of water in a graduated cylinder.

4. Add the water to the salt in the flask and stir until the salt is dissolved. This mixture will be the "seawater" in this investigation.

5. Clamp a support ring to a ring stand, and position it above a laboratory burner.

6. Place a wire gauze square on the support ring.

7. Set the flask of seawater on the wire gauze and secure it to the support stand with the flask clamp.

8. Connect the section of rubber hose to the glass tubing inserted in the stopper.

9. Fit the stopper into the mouth of the Erlenmeyer flask.

10. Place the free end of the rubber hose into the beaker.

## Goal
Demonstrate the distilling of seawater to remove the minerals (salt).

## Materials
table salt, 3.5 g
Erlenmeyer flask, 250 mL
graduated cylinder, 100 mL
water, 100 mL
ring stand
support ring
laboratory burner
wire gauze beaker support
flask clamp
one-hole stopper containing a short length of glass tubing
new rubber hose, 60 cm
beaker, 250 mL
matches or burner igniter

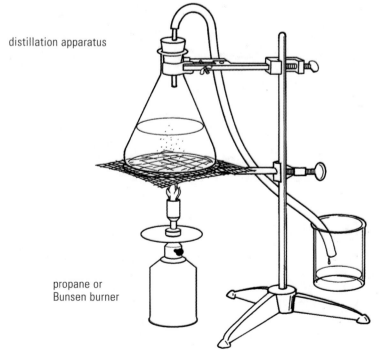

distillation apparatus

propane or
Bunsen burner

*Caution*: Steam is hot!

11. Light the laboratory burner.

12. Boil the seawater until only a few milliliters remain.

    *Caution*: Avoid the steam rising from the beaker. Also, the water in the beaker is hot. Allow it to cool before proceeding.

13. The beaker should contain purified water. Taste it. (*Note*: Do *not* taste the water if the flask, hose, or beaker have ever held laboratory chemicals.) Does it taste salty?

    _____

## Summing Up

1. According to your text, what is the method demonstrated in this investigation called? _____

2. Why isn't the method demonstrated in this investigation used very much today? _____

   _____

3. What other substances (besides water) could be recovered from seawater by this process? _____

   _____

# Investigation
# 19J Examining Density Currents

There are several reasons for the formation of ocean currents. The amount of material dissolved in the water determines its density. A difference in density between two depths is one cause of ocean currents. This investigation will help you to observe why different densities affect the currents.

## Procedure and observations

1. Fill two bottles with plain tap water from the container indicated by your teacher.

2. Mix a saturated salt solution in a 500 mL beaker using water from the same container. Fill the other two bottles with the saturated salt water.

3. Add several drops of food coloring into both bottles of salt water.

4. Arrange the bottles according to the diagram to the right. To invert a bottle without spilling the water, place an index card over the mouth. Holding the card firmly against the mouth, turn the bottle upside down and rest it against the mouth of the other bottle. Ease the index card out from between the two bottles.

5. Observe the two bottles over several minutes and record your observations.

   _____

   _____

   _____

6. In the space below, make a sketch of what happened within the bottles.

## Goal
Observe the formation of a density current.

## Materials
glass bottles (4) (250 mL glass reagent bottles or baby food jars)

table salt

tap water

beaker, 500 mL

food coloring

index card (2)

## Summing Up

1. What caused the water movement in one set of bottles? _____
_____
_____

2. Why was there no water movement in the other set of bottles? _____
_____
_____

3. What effect does gravity have on the flow of dense liquids above less dense liquids? _____
_____
_____

4. Could temperature have played a part in the color change? _____
_____
_____

# 20 GLACIERS

Applications

## 20A  Glacier Structure

*Directions*: Explain the difference between the terms in each pair of terms below. Label the diagram at the bottom of the page.

1.  glacier / snowfield _____

_____

_____

2.  firn / glacial ice _____

_____

_____

3.  accumulation zone / wastage zone _____

_____

_____

4.  valley glaciers / piedmont glaciers _____

_____

_____

5.  continental glacier / icecap _____

_____

_____

6.  zone of fracture / zone of flow _____

_____

_____

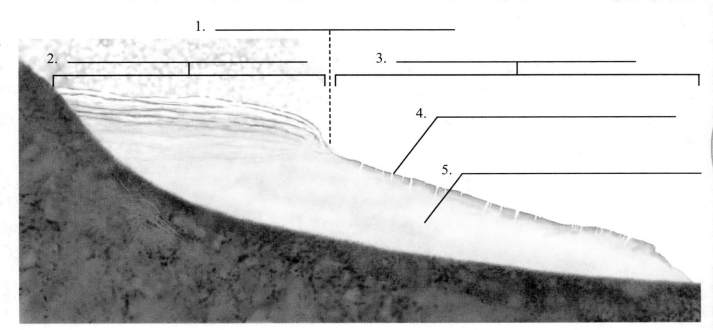

Applications

# 20B Types of Glaciers

*Directions*: Match the type of glacier with each description below.

_____ 1. Broad mass of ice that covers essentially all geographic features over a wide area

_____ 2. Means "at the foot of the mountain"

_____ 3. Large ice sheet covering most of a continent or large island

_____ 4. Found between mountains and in highlands

_____ 5. Spreads outward from its origin in all directions

_____ 6. Smaller type of ice sheet

_____ 7. Formed by the union of two or more valley glaciers in a broad basin or plain

_____ 8. The type of glacier covering more than four-fifths of Greenland

_____ 9. World's largest of this category is found in northern Ellesmere Island, Canada.

_____ 10. Resembles rivers of ice

a. Valley glacier
b. Piedmont glacier
c. Ice sheet
d. Icecap
e. Continental glacier

Applications

# 20C Effects of Glaciers

*Directions*: Change one word in each of the following sentences to make a correct statement. Cross out the incorrect word, and place the correct word in the blank.

_____ 1. The uppermost 50 m layer of a glacier, called the zone of fracture, consists of plastic ice.

_____ 2. Most glaciers can normally move a few meters or kilometers per day.

_____ 3. A horn may be all that is left of a valley if cirques completely encircle it.

_____ 4. A tarn is an inlet or arm of the sea dug out by glacial action and bordered by steep cliffs.

_____ 5. A glacier forms cirques to relieve the stresses of motion.

_____ 6. The world's largest valley glacier covers most of the continent of Antarctica.

_____ 7. Geologists are scientists who study glaciers.

_____ 8. Cirques that retain water after the glacier disappears are called kettles.

Applications

# 20D Glacial Deposits

*Directions*: Answer the following questions.

1. Explain the two ways that a glacier can deposit sediment (drift). _____
_____
_____
_____

2. When are deposits from glacier ice unsorted and unstratified? _____
_____
_____
_____

3. How is till deposited by a glacier? _____
_____
_____
_____

4. Define *moraine*. List four types of moraines. _____
_____
_____
_____

5. How are eskers and kames alike? How are they different? _____
_____
_____
_____

6. How were kettles formed? _____
_____
_____

7. What are varves? What events may cause varve counting to be unreliable? _____
_____
_____
_____

Applications

# 20E Glacier Review

*Directions*: Complete the crossword puzzle.

## Across

1. An ice _____ covers a large area.
7. An ice _____ covers the tops of mountains.
9. Any glacial deposit
10. A/An _____ moraine covers the whole area that a glacier occupied.
12. Snow-covered area above the snow line
13. Process in which the glacier ice adheres to the bedrock, which is torn out when the glacier moves
17–18. A/An __17__ __18__ points to a distant bedrock source.
22. A deep fissure in a glacier
23. Steep, hollow excavation made by a glacier on a mountain
24. A glacially produced lake
25. _____ glaciers are actually found in valleys.
27. Thin layers of fine glacial sediments on lake bottoms
28. _____ moraines are found at the sides of glacier valleys.
30. Probably deposited by a stream flowing under a glacier
34. A/An _____ moraine formed when two glaciers merged.
35. An accumulation of glacial drift
36. Another name for a valley glacier

## Down

2. Moraine deposited at the terminus of a glacier
3. Mountain peak surrounded by at least three cirques
4. The _____ zone is that part of a glacier that breaks up, melts, or flows away.
5. Type of glacier formed by the union of two or more valley glaciers in a broad area
6. A/An _____ glacier covers a large portion of a continent or large island.
8. Type of glacier found between mountain ridges
11. A streamlined hill of glacial till
12. Parallel scratch marks in bedrock
14. Process of forming icebergs
15. A mass of ice made by the compaction and refreezing of snow that moves under the influence of gravity
16. Coastal valley glacially eroded below sea level
19. The _____ zone is above the snow line.
20. The zone of _____ has crevasses.
21. Depression formed by a block of ice that melted
26. Dropped boulders unlike the bedrock under them
29. Unstratified glacial drift
31. A steep-sided hill of stratified glacial drift
32. Unusually rapid glacier movement
33. Granular ice

Investigation
# 20F Glacial Erosion

It is difficult in the average classroom to observe firsthand the action of glaciers in producing erosion. However, this investigation will help you observe a similar action.

## Goal
Make a simple model of a glacier to demonstrate how glaciers may erode the landscape.

## Materials
large dishpan

enough fine soil to fill the dishpan about 12–15 cm (5–6 in.) deep

ice cubes

## Procedure

1. At the side of the dishpan, partially bury four or five ice cubes in the soil. Leave the tops of some of the ice cubes showing and cover others completely with soil.

2. Put several ice cubes in a row extending out from one edge of the dishpan. Push the column of cubes with your finger or with a pencil to the other end of the dishpan. Observe the results.

3. Leave all the ice cubes in place and allow them to melt.

4. After the ice cubes have melted, carefully pour water into the holes that remain.

## Summing Up

1. What erosional features were formed by pushing a row of ice cubes across the surface of the soil?

   _____

2. What erosional features were formed by burying ice cubes and allowing them to melt? _____

   _____

3. Did it make any difference how deep the ice cubes were buried or with how much pressure they were moved across the surface of the soil?

   _____

   _____

4. What would the extent of glacial erosion in an area tell you about the size of the glacier that once covered it?

   _____

   _____

5. What does pouring water into the remaining holes demonstrate? _____

   _____

   _____

## Investigation
# 20G Representative Glaciers

Valley glaciers are still prevalent in the northwestern United States and Alaska. By studying topographic maps of these regions, you can see both their present locations and the results of their past erosional and depositional work. The glaciers and their tributaries appear white on the maps. Glacial drift, whether riding on the surface of a glacier or left as a deposit at the sides or end of a glacier, is indicated by dotted areas. Crevasses are represented by short line segments that mark where the cracks in the glacier were located at the time the map was made. Calving (iceberg formation) may be seen on a topographic map at the point a glacier enters a body of water. Erosional remains of mountains in glaciated areas take the form of arêtes or horns. Both of these features are identifiable by their closely spaced contour lines, the horns showing as single sharp peaks and the arêtes as elongated narrow ridges.

## Procedure and Observations

### PART 1: MOUNT RAINIER

Mount Rainier is a massive composite volcano located in the Cascade Mountains of Washington State. Its lofty stature and numerous glaciers combine to make it a picturesque sight, visible for many miles in every direction. At present it is a model of serenity, although some small steam emissions can be seen from time to time and seismologists have noted a slight increase in the number of minor shallow earthquakes under the volcano. Approximately five hundred years have passed since its last major eruption. The 1978 USGS map on the following page shows the glaciers clearly contrasted against their surroundings. Since this is a relatively recent map, the contour lines are marked in meters. The contour interval is 50 m (about 164 ft).

1. How many named glaciers are there on the flanks of the mountain? (Count only those that have the word *glacier* included in their name.)

   Total: _____

2. Using the scale of kilometers, determine the length of the longest glacier, assuming that it begins at the summit and is continuous. (Give answer to the nearest half kilometer).

   _____

   Determine the same in miles. _____

**Goal**
Study the activity of a number of present-day valley glaciers as well as several examples of continental glaciation features.

**Materials**
calculator
hand magnifying lens
ruler

3. The Nisqually Glacier as shown on this 1978 map was about 4 miles long, measuring from the summit of the mountain to the terminus of the glacier. It was observed to retreat a total of 4131 feet between 1857 and 1944. Note the moraine that was deposited during the retreat. What symbol is used to represent moraine material?

   _____

4. Many of the glaciers exhibit three different orders of steepness: very steep near the summit, moderately sloping in the middle reaches, and gently sloping near the terminus. Using your scale of kilometers, determine the gradient for these three regions of the Winthrop Glacier.

   Gradient near the summit:

   _____ m/km

   Gradient at the word *Winthrop*:

   _____ m/km

   Gradient north of the word *Glacier*:

   _____ m/km

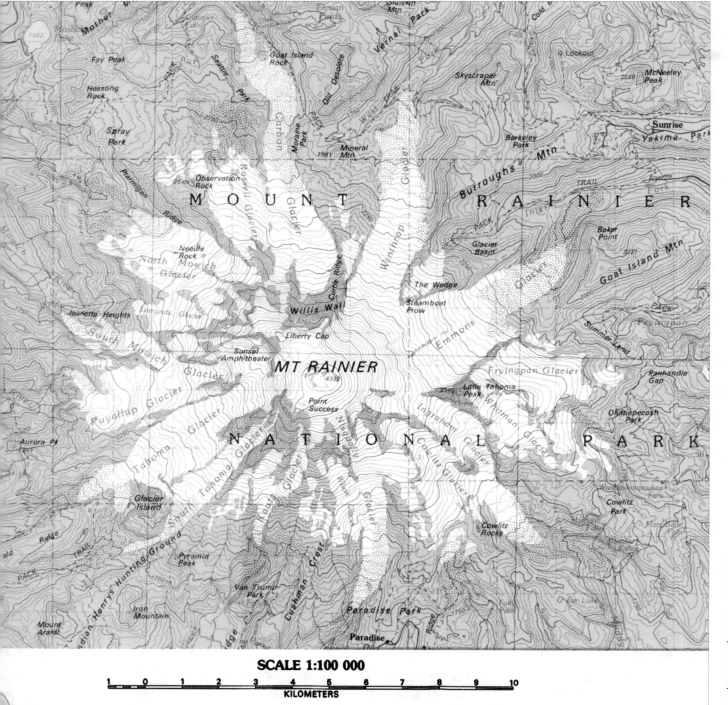

## SCALE 1:100 000

KILOMETERS

MILES

FEET

Mount Rainer Map (Part of the USGS Mount Rainier Quadrangle, Washington, 1978. Scale 1:100,000; Contour Interval 50 meters)

## PART 2: CORDOVA MAP

The map on the next page shows several valley glaciers in southeastern Alaska as mapped in 1953. Literally thousands of valley glaciers are contained within the boundaries of this large state, ranging in length from 2 to 48 kilometers (1–30 mi). In addition, there are large piedmont glaciers such as the Malaspina and Columbia Glaciers. Malaspina is the largest piedmont glacier in North America, having a width of almost 65 km (40 mi). This investigation will focus on the Heney and McCune Glaciers. Note that the map is subdivided into lettered 6 × 6 mile sections and numbered 1-square-mile subsections.

1. Judging by the contour lines, in which direction does Heney Glacier move?

   Toward the _____ (northeast, southwest)

2. Give the location and number(s) of the map subsection(s) in which calving could be taking place.

   _____

3. A long, unnamed tributary valley glacier joins Heney Glacier from the west.

   The lateral moraines of both the glacier and its tributary merge to form a _____ moraine.

4. The margins of the glaciers are marked with small dashed lines. Note that the McCune glacier dies out; it does not reach a lake or river as does the Heney Glacier. What becomes of its wasting ice?

   _____

   _____

5. A reasonably good example of a horn appears in map subsection D2. What is the elevation of its summit?

   _____

6. Several examples of arêtes appear on the map. One of the better ones is located in map subsections A24 and A25. What is the highest point on the arête?

   _____

7. What kind of glacial erosional feature is shown in the eastern portion of map subsection B5?

   _____

Cordova Map (Part of the USGS Cordova D-3 Quadrangle, Alaska, 1953. Scale 1:63,360; Contour Interval 100 feet)

# PART 3: WHITEWATER MAP

The maps (on p. SA282) for this part of the exercise are of two segments of a heavily glaciated region of southern Wisconsin. Several glacial features are shown here, including drumlins, kettles, and different kinds of moraines. A major difference between this region and the last two glaciated terrains you studied is that the deposits in Wisconsin were caused by a continental glacier. The glaciation that occurred in Washington and Alaska was connected with valley glaciers.

1. Numerous drumlins appear in the upper map. In what general direction are the drumlins oriented—east-west, north-south, northeast-southwest, or northwest-southeast?

   _____

2. What direction did the ice sheet move according to the orientation of the drumlins?

   _____

3. Locate Duck Creek to the west of the city of Rome. Study the high drumlin just to the west of the word "Duck." Assuming that its summit is halfway between contour lines, what is its elevation?

   _____

4. On the lower map, the irregular terrain south and east of Palmyra is part of a terminal moraine. Note that the average elevation in this region is greater than the elevation west of Palmyra. This is logical because the moraine is made up of "extra" material that was transported into the area by the glacier. What is the approximate elevation at the base of the radio tower in the northeast corner of grid square 35?

   _____

5. An example of a kettle appears in the west side of grid square 35. Note the hatched contour lines indicating that it is a depression. Assuming that the floor of the kettle is halfway between contour lines, what is its elevation?

   _____

6. What kind of body of water is in the north side of grid square 31?

   _____

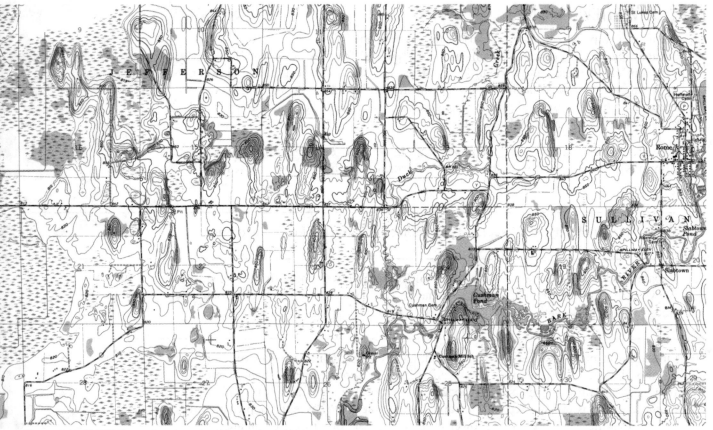

(Part of the USGS Rome Quadrangle, Wisconsin, 1960/1971. Scale 1:24,000; Contour Interval 10 feet)

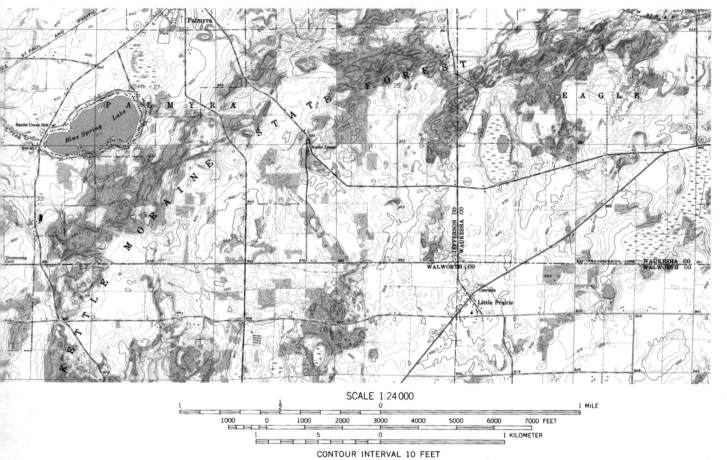

SCALE 1:24 000

CONTOUR INTERVAL 10 FEET

(Part of the USGS Little Prairie Quadrangle, Wisconsin, 1960/1971. Scale 1:24,000; Contour Interval 10 feet)

# 21 THE GROUNDWATER SYSTEM

Applications

## 21A The Hydrologic Cycle

*Directions*: Match the numbered items on the water cycle diagram with their labels by writing the proper letter choices in the blanks provided.

1. _____

2. _____

3. _____

4. _____

5. _____

6. _____

7. _____

8. _____

9. _____

a. Evaporation
b. Groundwater to bodies of water
c. Groundwater to water table
d. Groundwater to streams
e. Groundwater to vegetation
f. Precipitation
g. Run-off
h. Transpiration
i. Cloud formation (condensation)

Applications

# 21B Groundwater

*Directions*: In the puzzle below, write the words that are described by the following statements. Each term is related to the subject of groundwater.

1. A/An _____ is a location where the water table reaches the surface.

2. A/An _____ rock contains a large number of open spaces between its particles.

3. A cone-shaped lowering of the water table around a well is called a cone of _____.

4. The zone of _____ is the water-filled region below the water table.

5. A small region between the zone of aeration and the zone of saturation where water has worked its way upward is called the capillary _____.

6. A/An _____ water table is located in strata above the regular water table.

7. The level below which all the spaces between rocks or soil particles are filled with water is called the _____ table.

8. The ground above the water table is called the zone of _____.

9. A/An _____ well occurs where the water rises to the ground surface under its own pressure in a well pipe.

10. Material that allows liquids or gases to pass through it is _____.

11. The path that water takes between the ocean, the clouds, precipitation, groundwater, and the ocean again is called the _____ cycle.

1. __ __ __ __ __ | G |
2. __ __ | R | __ __ __
3. __ __ __ __ __ __ __ __ | O | __
4. __ __ __ | U | __ __ __ __ __ __
5. __ __ __ | N | __ __
6. __ __ __ __ __ __ | D |
7. | W | __ __ __ __
8. __ __ __ | A | __ __ __ __
9. __ __ | T | __ __ __ __ __
10. __ __ __ __ | E | __ __ __
11. __ __ __ | R | __ __ __ __ __

Applications

# 21C Hard and Soft Water

*Directions*: In the spaces provided to the left, write *True* if the statement is true and *False* if the statement is false. For *False* answers, state why the answer is false in the blanks provided.

_____ 1. Although it may look like pure water, groundwater always contains various dissolved minerals.

_____

_____

_____

_____ 2. Dissolved minerals in water supplies are usually harmful to humans.

_____

_____

_____

_____ 3. Hard water contains high concentrations of dissolved calcium or magnesium compounds.

_____

_____

_____

_____ 4. Soft water is low in calcium and magnesium compounds.

_____

_____

_____

_____ 5. Lathering soap in soft water is difficult because a chemical reaction makes the soap less active.

_____

_____

_____

_____ 6. Scum that forms on bathtubs is caused by a chemical reaction between soap and hard water.

_____

_____

_____

## Applications

# 21D  Karst Topography

*Directions*: Match the features listed below with the corresponding areas on the diagram. Place the letter for each feature in the appropriate box. Then write a definition in the space provided for each of the terms listed.

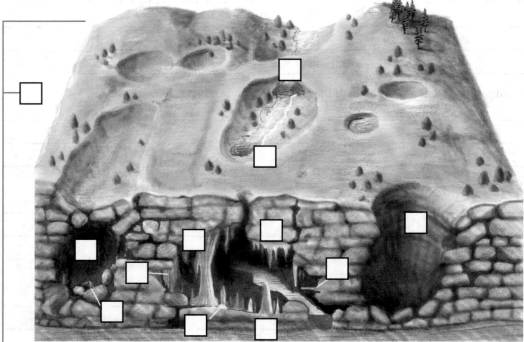

a. Column
b. Curtain
c. Disappearing stream
d. Karst topography
e. Natural bridge
f. Shelf
g. Shield
h. Sinkhole
i. Solution cave
j. Spelunker
k. Stalactites
l. Stalagmites

1. Cave _____
_____

2. Column _____
_____

3. Disappearing stream _____
_____

4. Flowstone _____
_____

5. Karst topography _____
_____

6. Natural bridge _____
_____

7. Sinkhole _____
_____

8. Spelunker _____
_____

9. Stalactites _____
_____

10. Stalagmites _____
_____

Investigation
# 21E Permeability

## Procedure

1. Use a grease pencil to label the cups 1, 2, and 3.

2. Mix some plaster of Paris in a bucket.

3. Arrange strata of gravel, sand, clay, and plaster in each cup according to the following table. Be sure that no layer leaves any openings at the edges of the cup.

| Cup | 1 | 2 | 3 |
|---|---|---|---|
| Strata order | gravel<br>sand<br>plaster<br>clay | plaster<br>clay<br>sand<br>gravel | plaster<br>sand<br>clay<br>gravel |

4. Allow the cups to stand until the plaster hardens.

5. Pour water into each cup and record the results (how far the water penetrates) in the table below.

6. Make a small crack in the plaster layers in cups 2 and 3. Observe the water. Record the results in the table below.

### Goal
Demonstrate the permeability of different arrangements of sedimentary rock layers.

### Materials
grease pencil
plastic cups (clear) (3)
plaster of Paris
bucket
gravel
sand
clay
water

| Cup | Initial water penetration | Water penetration after plaster cracked |
|---|---|---|
| 1 | | |
| 2 | | |
| 3 | | |

## Summing Up

1. What are sedimentary rocks? (*Hint*: Refer to Chapter 15 if necessary.) _____
_____

2. What are layers of sedimentary rock called? _____

3. Which of the four materials in this investigation were permeable? _____

   Which were impermeable or nearly so? _____

4. Which cup with the cracked plaster could be considered the recharge zone for a deep aquifer?

_____

Investigation
# 21F Mineral Water

Water picks up minerals as it moves through the ground. The presence of these minerals in water can be both desirable and undesirable. Since we need minerals for our bodies to function properly, drinking mineral water can have healthful benefits. Europeans have been "taking the waters" at spas for centuries. Today we can purchase mineral water that was bottled at its source. Although possibly healthful, waters with a mineral content may taste terrible, smell unpleasant, and cause soap to form a scum rather than a lather. For reasons such as these, most communities remove the minerals from water in their water purification process.

Water that contains high concentrations of dissolved minerals is called hard water; water that contains low concentrations of dissolved minerals is called soft water. Minerals that commonly cause hard water are calcium or magnesium compounds. These compounds may be further classified as bicarbonates, sulfates, or chlorides. There are several products on the market that can remove unwanted minerals from water.

## Procedure and Observations

### PART 1: SMELL AND TASTE OF MINERAL WATER

1. Pour some mineral water into a small cup. Smell the mineral water. Describe the smell.

   _____

   _____

2. Taste the mineral water. Describe the taste.

   _____

   _____

### PART 2: EFFECT ON SOAPSUDS

1. Fill each of four test tubes about half full with one of the following types of water (each test tube gets a different kind of water): distilled water, mineral water, tap water, and distilled water with Epsom salts. (*Note*: Add a very small pinch of Epsom salts to the test tube.)

2. Add one drop of liquid soap to each test tube.

3. Cap each test tube with your thumb and shake the tube vigorously for 10 seconds to make soapsuds.

## Goal
Use the senses of smell and taste to examine mineral water. Demonstrate the effect hard water has on soap's lathering.

## Materials
mineral water
test tubes (4)
distilled water
tap water
Epsom salts
liquid soap (dish-washing soap, not detergent)
small cup

4. Wait 1 minute; then observe the suds in each test tube. Which test tube has the most suds?

   _____

   How does the appearance of the water in each test tube differ?

   _____

   _____

## Summing Up

1. Was the smell and taste of the mineral water pleasant or unpleasant? _____

2. What was produced after adding Epsom salts to the water? _____

3. What did the presence of lots of soapsuds indicate? _____
   _____

4. What did the absence of lots of soapsuds indicate? _____
   _____

5. Where in your home would it be especially beneficial to use soft water? _____
   _____

6. Are benefits of bathing in mineral water primarily due to a better cleaning ability? _____
   _____

# 21G Stalactites and Stalagmites

## Procedure

1. Fill the beakers with warm water.

2. Put Epsom salts into the beakers and stir to dissolve. Continue adding Epsom salts until no more will dissolve.

3. Soak the string thoroughly in one of the beakers.

4. Set the two beakers on the tray 4 to 8 cm apart and drape the string between them, with each end of the string submerged in a separate beaker.

5. Set the tray in a place where it will be undisturbed for several days and out of direct sunlight.

6. After three to five days, inspect the apparatus and record the results.

### Goal
Observe the formation of stalactites and stalagmites.

### Materials
beakers (250 mL) (2)
water
Epsom salts
heavy cotton string, 30 cm
tray

## Summing Up

1. Where do the deposits come from? _____

_____

2. What causes the Epsom salts to reappear? _____

_____

3. How does this process represent the formation of stalactites and stalagmites in caves? _____

_____

_____

_____

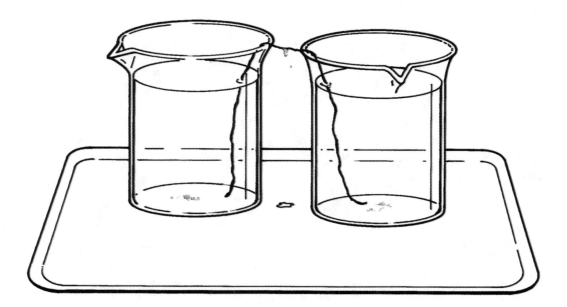

# 21H Solution of Limestone

Some caves and other formations typical of karst to-pography are formed by the solution (dissolving) of lime-stone or other soluble rocks by groundwater. While the origin of solution caves is open to discussion, it is known today that groundwater can dissolve limestone because the water is slightly acidic and thus reacts with the lime-stone. In this investigation you will determine the amount of limestone dissolved during one week of exposure to slightly acidic water.

## Procedure and Observations

1. Choose pieces of limestone for this experiment that are about the same size and shape. (*Note*: Size, shape, and weight are important since the goal is to have equal limestone surface areas in each treat-ment.) Rinse the limestones thoroughly in water and allow them to dry.

2. Accurately find the mass of five samples of the limestone pieces. Each sample should be about 10 g. Record the starting mass in the table and place each sample in a separate flask.

3. Prepare the slightly acidic solutions as follows:

   *Water*: Measure 100 mL of water, using the gradu-ated cylinder. Pour this into one of the flasks with limestones. Label the flask "#1, Water."

   *Humic Acid*: Using the graduated cylinder, meas-ure 100 mL of the water from the humus container prepared by your teacher. Pour the solution into one of the unlabeled flasks. Label the flask "#2, Humic Acid." Rinse out the graduated cylinder with tap water.

   *1 N HCl*: Your teacher will provide you with a 1 *N* solution of hydrochloric acid. Measure 100 mL of this using the graduated cylinder. Pour this into one of the unlabeled flasks. Label the flask "#3, 1 *N* HCl." *Caution*: Hydrochloric acid can cause ir-ritation or burns. Avoid getting acid in your eyes.

   *Vinegar*: Measure 100 mL of vinegar using the graduated cylinder. Pour this into one of the unla-beled flasks. Label the flask "#4, Vinegar."

   *Carbonic Acid*: Measure 100 mL of carbonated water using the graduated cylinder. Pour this into the remaining unlabeled flask. Label the flask "#5, Carbonic Acid."

## Goal
Measure the dissolving of limestone by slightly acidic solutions.

## Materials
limestone pieces (similar-sized), 40–50 g

balance (accurate to 0.1 g)

flasks, (125 mL) (5)

graduated cylinder (100 mL)

water, 4–5 L

rubber stoppers (5)

1 *N* HCl (hydrochloric acid), 100 mL

vinegar, 100 mL

carbonic acid (carbonated water or soft drink), 100 mL

universal pH indicator paper or pH meter

| Flask | Solution | pH | Starting mass | Ending mass | Change in mass | Percent change |
|-------|----------|-----|---------------|-------------|----------------|----------------|
| 1 | Water | | g | g | g | % |
| 2 | Humic acid | | g | g | g | % |
| 3 | 1 *N* HCL | | g | g | g | % |
| 4 | Vinegar | | g | g | g | % |
| 5 | Carbonic acid | | g | g | g | % |

4.  Determine the pH of each solution with universal pH indicator paper or a pH meter and record the values.

5.  Loosely stopper the flasks to limit evaporation. Place all the flasks in the same area so that they will encounter the same temperature and other conditions.

6.  After one week pour off each solution and recover the limestone pieces. Rinse each limestone sample *separately* and allow them to dry on paper towels.

7.  When the limestone samples are completely dry, measure the mass of each and record the ending mass in the table. Subtract the ending mass from the starting mass for each sample. Record the change in mass.

8.  Divide the change in mass by the starting mass of each sample. Multiply the result by 100 to obtain percent change for each solution. Record this value in the last column of the table.

## Summing Up

1.  Which solution produced the largest percent change in mass? _____

_____

2.  Where did the lost matter go? _____

_____

3.  Did any sample not lose any measurable mass? _____ Why? _____

_____

4.  What was the relationship between the pH and the amount of limestone dissolved? _____

_____

5.  How do the results here demonstrate how some speleothems form? _____

_____

6.  Which of these acids are present in groundwater long after the Flood? _____

_____

## Go a Step Further

Repeat this investigation, using other kinds of rocks as well as limestone. Compare the rates of solution of the various rocks. Is limestone the only one that dissolves?

_____

What rocks dissolve more rapidly? _____

What do your results indicate about where caves are likely to form?

_____

_____

# PHOTOGRAPH CREDITS

These agencies and individuals have furnished materials to meet the photographic needs of this textbook. We wish to express our gratitude to them for their important contribution:

Anglo-Australian Observatory
Cartesia Software
Albert Copley
Gerald and Buffi Corsi
Chuck Doswell
Earth Science World
Forestry Images
Akira Fuji
Getty Images
Jet Propulsion Lab (JPL)

Brian D. Johnson
Breck Kent
Dr. Ken McDonald
David Malin Images (DMI)
Mount Washington Observatory
National Aeronautics and Space
  Administration (NASA)
Joseph O'Brien
Oklahoma University
Pekka Parviainen

PhotoDisc
Photo Researchers, Inc.
Science Photo Library
USDA Forestry Services
United States Geological Survey (USGS)
Visuals Unlimited
Stephan Wüthrich
Frank Zullo

## Cover
PhotoDisc/Getty Images clouds, grass

## Front Matter
PhotoDisc/Getty Images iii

## Chapter 1
SeaWIFS Project, NASA, Goddard Space Flight Center and ORBIMAGE SA3

## Chapter 2
NASA SA11

## Chapter 3
Anglo-Australian Observatory/David Malin Images SA27; NASA SA33 (both), SA34 (all)

## Chapter 4
Pekka Parviainen SA49

## Chapter 5
NASA SA63

## Chapter 6
Akira Fuji/David Malin Images SA83

## Chapter 7
© Frank Zullo/Photo Researchers, Inc. SA95; NASA SA96, SA100

## Chapter 8
NASA/JPL SA111; based on NASA imagery SA111 (middle and bottom)

## Chapter 9
Brian D. Johnson SA125

## Chapter 10
Joseph O'Brian, USDA Forestry Services/www.forestryimages.org SA133

## Chapter 11
© Chuck Doswell/Visuals Unlimited SA143

## Chapter 12
Mount Washington Observatory SA159

## Chapter 13
© Oklahoma University; www.earthscienceworld.org SA183

## Chapter 14
© Albert Copley/Visuals Unlimited SA191

## Chapter 15
Breck Kent SA203

## Chapter 16
PhotoDisc/Getty Images SA217; USGS SA227, SA229

## Chapter 17
USGS SA223, SA246; Cartesia Software SA237; based on USGS map SA244

## Chapter 18
© Gerald and Buffi Corsi/Visuals Unlimited SA247

## Chapter 19
Dr. Ken McDonald/Science Photo Library SA257

## Chapter 20
Dr. Ken McDonald/Science Photo Library SA271; USGS SA278, SA280; SA282 (both)

## Chapter 21
Stephan Wüthrich, Zurich, Switzerland SA283